The Enemy Within

The Struggle To Clean Up Cape Cod's Military Superfund Site

BY SETH ROLBEIN

Published by the

Association for the Preservation of Cape Cod

EDITED BY DAN HAMILTON

Distributed by   Association for the Preservation of Cape Cod
P.O. Box 636
Orleans, MA 02653
Tel. (508) 255-4142
FAX (508) 255-8780

THE ENEMY WITHIN: The Struggle To Clean Up Cape Cod's Military Superfund Site is available for purchase directly from the Association for the Preservation of Cape Cod offices. Special discounts are available for bulk purchases for non-profit organizations, or educational use.

The Association for the Preservation of Cape Cod is an independent, grassroots environmental advocacy group serving all of Cape Cod and dedicated to preserving the Cape's natural resources and unique character. APCC's independence and influence depend on its base of paid memberships. To join in support of APCC's work, please call or write APCC for membership information.

Printed by   Shankpainter Printing Company
Shankpainter Road
Provincetown, MA 02657

Printed on recycled paper.

About Our Book Cover and Enclosed Map

The Massachusetts Military Reservation (MMR) interpretive groundwater contamination map represents the culmination of over 10 years of investigation work at the MMR to identify and quantify environmental problems associated with various contamination sites. The nine* plumes of groundwater contamination were defined using groundwater quality information from hundreds of monitoring wells installed at various depths throughout the military base and in neighboring areas. Darker areas within each plume represent zones of higher concentrations of pollution.

    * A 10th plume has been identified at the Fuel Spill 1 site, but field work is incomplete, and the zone has yet to be reflected on the National Guard Bureau's official plume map.

7·14·09

To: Brian & Nancy
This book would even curl
the feathers on your ducks !!

Mike Mason

Contents

STATEMENT

The text of *The Enemy Within: The Struggle To Clean Up Cape Cod's Miltary Superfund Site* does not necessarily reflect the views or opinions of the Massachusetts Department of Environmental Protection, the Sudbury Foundation or individual contributors to this project.

INTRODUCTION

The Association for the Preservation of Cape Cod (APCC) was organized by a group of citizens in 1968 to fight the long term battle for Cape Cod's environmental survival. Protection of the Cape's groundwater has always been a top priority for APCC. Groundwater is the mainstay of the region's existence - it provides drinking water to all the Cape's residents; it feeds every lake, pond and vernal pool on Cape Cod; and it creates a brackish environment along our coast where fresh water discharges from the aquifer, establishing a habitat for thousands of terrestrial and aquatic life forms.

APCC has a long history of involvement with groundwater protection on Cape Cod. During the 1970s, APCC worked Capewide to gain support for a referendum to fund a study of the Cape's groundwater system by the U.S. Geological Survey. The work done by USGS and APCC led to funding of an extensive "208" program for Cape Cod - a multi-year water quality and wastewater disposal planning grant from the federal government under Section 208 of the Federal Water Pollution Control Act. With substantial involvement by APCC, Cape Cod was designated as a "sole source aquifer" by the U.S. Environmental Protection Agency in 1982, creating broad public awareness of the Cape's water supply system and its fragility.

Throughout the 1980s, APCC played a pivotal role in convincing towns to adopt stricter land use zoning and regulations in order to protect the vulnerable water supply. Between 1988 and 1990, APCC committed substantial resources to help create a regional land use planning and regulatory agency, the Cape Cod Commission, in large part to help protect groundwater quality from the adverse impacts of untoward development.

Cape Cod faces many threats to its groundwater quality. The most widespread is the proliferation of household septic and cesspool systems across the Cape, which daily discharge thousands of gallons of polluted water to the very aquifer from which the Cape's drinking water supply is drawn. Compounding this problem are other discharges to the aquifer. Solid waste landfills create underground plumes of toxic chemicals; leaking underground fuel tanks contaminate zones of groundwater with gasoline; wastewater treatment plants discharge massive quantities of pollutants; road runoff concentrates contaminants from paved surfaces which then migrate to the aquifer; and lawn and turf chemicals seep into the groundwater system from the land surface.

For decades, we have been using our groundwater aquifer as both a pollutant catchment and a water supply source. The legacy of our own negligence is a host of impending water quality and quantity crises across Cape Cod. On the Upper Cape, water quality problems are seriously compounded by 10 plumes of toxic groundwater contamination spreading out from the Massachusetts Military Reservation (MMR). Across the Upper Cape towns of Bourne, Falmouth, Mashpee, Sandwich, and Barnstable, the population has more than doubled in the past two decades. Demand for water has similarly increased, but the options for new water supply development have sharply declined as areas once suitable for siting wells have been subdivided and developed. When the disaster of the Massachusetts Military Reservation contamination came to light in 1979, the gradually narrowing window between water demand and available supply on the upper Cape suddenly slammed nearly shut. Today the four towns surrounding the base are faced with a double headed dilemma - acutely increased demand for water due to the dramatically increased population, and considerably decreased supply areas, not only because of development, but because the immense pollution plumes spreading out from the base destroy another eight million gallons of potable water every day.

As the extent of groundwater pollution at the Massachusetts Military Reservation became increasingly evident, APCC moved to put the base cleanup at the top of its agenda. Clearly, the pollution plumes at the MMR Superfund site constitute the most massive contamination on all of Cape Cod, with the potential of wiping out numerous existing and future public water supplies in four, if not five, communities. APCC is compelled to do its utmost to stop and clean up these underground zones of migrating ruin.

Yet, the MMR pollution problems have historically been difficult to expose. Political and economic implications have made the military, local town governments, the state, and some businesses reluctant to talk openly or urgently about the base contamination. The real estate industry may be particularly affected, as suggested by the unusually low $90,000 price tag on some new homes between Ashumet and John's Ponds, in the heart of the impact

vi

area for five plumes. The issue of contamination of groundwater at MMR is, however, commanding for all of Cape Cod, since the extirpation of water supplies drains tax dollars, devalues property, reduces the attractiveness of the area to investors and vacationers, and puts undue pressure on alternative water supply sources.

In spite of the monumental challenge posed by the MMR situation, a multitude of people has worked relentlessly over the last fifteen years to achieve accountability by the military. Their story is told in "The Enemy Within - The Struggle to Clean Up Cape Cod's Military Superfund Site."

APCC is just one of the players that has been integrally involved in the effort to get the Department of Defense to correct pollution problems at MMR. The purpose in publishing this book is to inform and empower residents of Cape Cod, and places beyond, where similar situations exist. By presenting a comprehensive picture of the pollution situation at MMR, from historic activities, to discovery and delineation of the plumes, to community activism to address the crisis, APCC hopes to build public awareness and understanding, and ultimately to involve a greater number of people in a greater number of ways to hasten cleanup of MMR.

"The Enemy Within" also looks at the inner workings of the military environmental cleanup bureaucracy. It reveals the What and Why behind the conspicuous footdragging, secrecy and intimidation by the National Guard Bureau that have often typified its response to the MMR situation. The book takes a critical look at what happens when the military is faced with responsibility for serious damage to the environment and possibly public health in a heavily populated and popular region of the country.

In 1981, Cape Cod writer and naturalist Bob Finch described in his book "Common Ground", "an oversimplified stereotyped myth of national nostalgia known as Old Cape Cod," and pointed out the pitfalls of "false thinking and false seeing about a vulnerable land" in regard to the despoliation suffered by decades of human exploitation. No better example of this paradox exists on Cape Cod than the unintentional but nonetheless negligent dumping and disposal of millions of gallons of hazardous wastes at the Massachusetts Military Reservation throughout the majority of this century.

It is ironic that a region of the country with such a widespread reputation for pristine beaches and rural, unsullied landscapes should be plagued by an environmental problem of these dimensions. The Cape Cod of our imagination - relaxing seascapes, weathered shingled antique houses, and rambler roses on a split rail fence in mid-summer - is hard to reconcile with the glaring reality that this beautiful peninsula is home to the worst Air National Guard Bureau Superfund site in the country. And so in addition to improving public grasp of the depth and breadth of the MMR problem, APCC offers this book as a way to help mend a distressing dichotomy that should not exist.

Being as closely involved in the MMR problem as APCC is, and trying to write a fair book on the subject, was definitely a challenge. But with a Board of Directors convinced of the importance of the project, APCC contracted with a well-established investigative journalist and author to carry out the work. The product of the efforts of APCC and author Seth Rolbein is contained in the pages that follow. The APCC Board of Directors sincerely hopes that "The Enemy Within - The Struggle to Clean Up Cape Cod's Military Superfund Site" will stand as a substantial contribution to the progress of cleanup at MMR, and will serve as a resource and catalyst for action at other military toxic sites around the nation. The lessons learned from MMR are lessons to be shared across the country as more and more military toxic sites demand attention, and the public is motivated to act.

Susan L. Nickerson
Executive Director
APCC

****

Any writing on the Massachusetts Military Reservation cleanup issue is, of necessity, a snapshot in time. As "The Enemy Within" goes to press, a number of significant developments have taken place:

The new military administration involved in the MMR project, described at the end of the book, initially turned back the march of progress that characterized the cleanup effort during the past two years. After National Guard Bureau personnel changes occurred in the summer of 1994, the pace of the plume containment effort came to a near standstill. Contracting problems and bureaucratic mismanagement ate up eight precious months during which the system design for containment of the plumes could have been progressing. New policies were implemented that appear designed to curtail public involvement, limit the flow of information to area citizens, and fragment coalitions that have developed in the community.

For example, in January, 1995, the head of the Environmental Division of the Air National Guard Bureau announced that the citizen Process Action Team that played a vital role in development of the plume containment plan, and gaining public acceptance for it, would be disbanded as "its job was done". This assertion came despite the long months ahead for design and construction of the plume containment system, for which community support is essential. A firestorm of protest over the announcement ensued, and the decision was reversed. Despite the eventual acknowledgement of public sentiment, the distrust engendered by that maneuver will not be easily overcome, and strained rapport with the community may well continue to fetter the cleanup process.

These problems locally are exacerbated by recent developments on the national scene. The new Congress is in the process of making severe cuts in military cleanup spending, not only from future budgets, but from the current fiscal year appropriation as well. Millions of dollars are on the chopping block for the MMR cleanup work in 1995. What these grim developments mean for the success of the MMR cleanup, and for the health and environment of Cape Cod, or the rest of the nation for that matter, is highly unsettling. Whether the National Guard Bureau will actually accomplish rapid containment and cleanup of the plumes at MMR, or if the effort presently underway is too little, too late, remains the crucial question.

What is apparent from the change in the political direction in Washington and on Cape Cod, is that greater uncertainty now exists, and that community involvement and dedication to get the Massachusetts Military Reservation cleanup done is immensely vital and as indispensable as ever. With this backdrop, the story told in "The Enemy Within" is wholly compelling.

ACKNOWLEDGEMENTS

An APCC book about a subject as complex as the Massachusetts Military Reservation could only happen because of the success of APCC's previous book, "State of the Cape 1994; Progress Toward Preservation." The response to "State of the Cape" from our members and the public told us that indeed educational material of this sort is extremely useful in helping citizens to coalesce and act on environmental issues facing the Cape. The "State of the Cape" book also convinced our funders of APCC's capabilities in this realm, and made grantseeking for this endeavor successful.

The compilation of material for "The Enemy Within; The Struggle To Clean Up Cape Cod's Military Superfund Site" was a monumental task, which our author Seth Rolbein undertook with unsurpassed zeal and enthusiasm. The work involved dozens of interviews, extensive legwork to track down information, and poring over a multitude of reports, files, and photographs. Our appreciation to him for formulating a book we are proud to publish.

The story told in "The Enemy Within" is woven substantially from the words of the people involved - the activists, other local citizens, local and state elected officials, regulators, National Guard Bureau personnel, state and federal agencies, local water purveyors, research institutions, universities, active and retired civilian personnel, retired military personnel, elected and appointed officials, and journalists. APCC thanks all who participated in providing intelligence for this book for their cooperation and sharing of vital information.

Special thanks go to the staff of Congressman Gerry Studds for assisting in the acquisition of important information from the Pentagon for this book.

We also appreciate the fine graphic design work provided by Anne Marie Oliver-Nickerson (AMON Graphics), photographs provided by Barry Donahue and Josh Albright of Cape Cod Community Newspapers, Paul Ott of the Falmouth Enterprise, and civilian and military staff at the Massachusetts Military Reservation. We thank the Cape Cod Times for kind assistance in production of the book cover. APCC is grateful to Shankpainter Printing for its cooperation and service.

For a thorough and professional editing job, APCC thanks Dan Hamilton.

Last, but certainly not least, APCC thanks the funders who made this project possible: the Sudbury Foundation, the Massachusetts Department of Environmental Protection (DEP) Technical Assistance Grant Program, and generous contributors to APCC's 25th Anniversary Fund Drive.

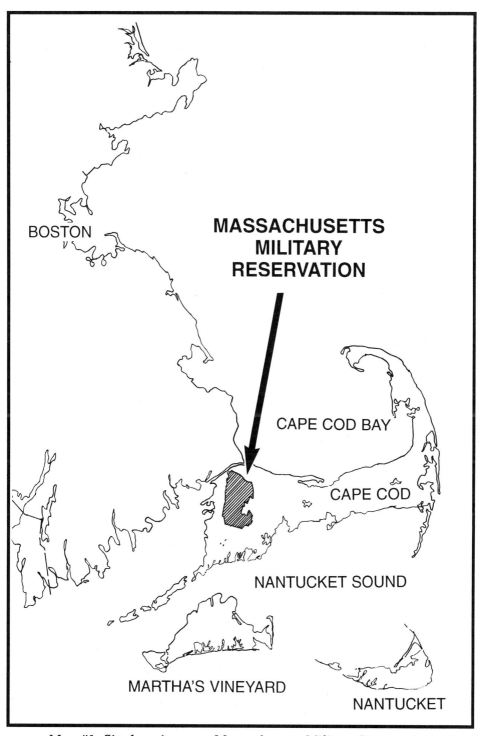

BOSTON

**MASSACHUSETTS
MILITARY
RESERVATION**

CAPE COD BAY

CAPE COD

NANTUCKET SOUND

MARTHA'S VINEYARD

NANTUCKET

Map #1 Site location map Massachusetts Military Reservation.

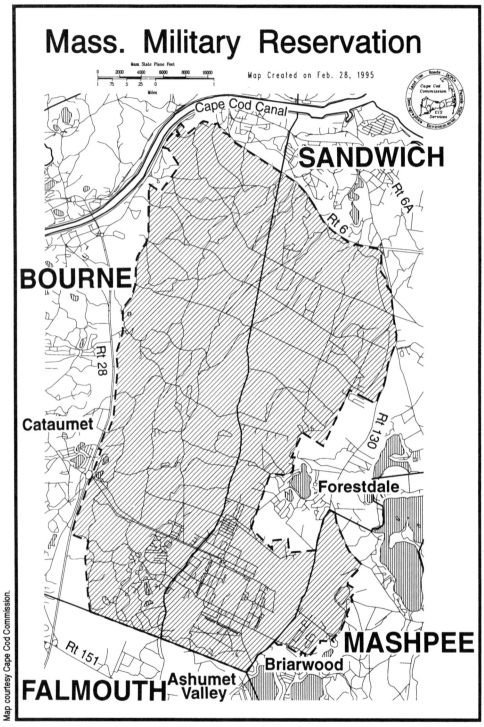

Mass. Military Reservation

Map Created on Feb. 28, 1995

Cape Cod Canal

SANDWICH

Rt 6A

Rt 6

BOURNE

Rt 28

Cataumet

Rt 130

Forestdale

MASHPEE

Rt 151

Briarwood

FALMOUTH Ashumet Valley

Map courtesy Cape Cod Commission.

Map #2 Massachusetts Military Reservation boundary.

1

A WATERSHED PLACE, A WATERSHED MOMENT

July 7, 1994. The dignitaries were seated under a blazing sun, the flat, broad landscape of the Massachusetts Military Reservation broken by a small building behind them. Inside that building was the only respite from the heat, because huge tanks holding underground water stood in the shade, acting as air conditioners.

That wasn't why they were there, of course, to serve as multi-million-dollar air conditioners. Their purpose was something else entirely:

The water is being pumped out of the ground and held in these tanks so it can be treated. This water bears telltale remnants of pollution dumped decades ago. This water must now be filtered to remove poisons left from the past.

It was a fitting place to hold this ceremony, between hot sun and cool groundwater, beside the first small treatment plant on the giant base. The chairs and tables where politicians and military brass sat side by side, where community activists, newspaper reporters and television cameramen focused their attention, were all directly above one of many so-called "plumes" buried deep underground, a spreading pool of contamination no longer ignored or denied, one of many invisible catastrophes which have caused so much

3

concern for thousands of people who live and work around Camp Edwards and Otis Air National Guard Base. This was the appropriate place because after more than a decade of study, argument, delay and frustration, Cape Cod was about to hear a promise: the federal government will spend hundreds of millions of dollars to try to stop these plumes from reaching even farther into the neighborhoods of Falmouth, Bourne, Mashpee, and Sandwich.

"This statement is a commitment," announced United States Senator Edward Kennedy, "which will be kept by the Department of Defense."

"We all understand," intoned United States Senator John Kerry, "that what is right underneath us as we sit here is a killer substance—of human beings, and of the spirit of communities."

"What you've done, and the way you've done it, will serve as a model to the whole nation," United States Congressman Gerry Studds concluded. "And the legacy might not be just clean sand and water, but good clean jobs too."

If Congressman Studds is right, then the personal stories of how people became involved in the fight for this cleanup, how Cape Cod residents convinced the military and the politicians that this work had to be done, becomes nationally important. Their stories could serve as testimony, as example and even inspiration for people elsewhere who also have a military base for a neighbor.

Some of the people who have dedicated years to this effort, spent count-less hours in meetings, labored over thousands of pages of documents, done everything from digging wells to lobbying officials to getting arrested, were sitting in the hot sun that July day. Others were not. Either way, many of them seem to have vivid memories of their first steps down this long road, when they first realized that something was wrong at Cape Cod's military base:

Dr. Joel Feigenbaum, a mathematics professor at Cape Cod Community College, says that moment came in the early 1980s as he watched smoke and debris from a huge fire blowing over Sandwich, a fire caused by artillery shells exploding on a dry, windy day. He stood with a hose in his hand, protecting his house from sparks. He wondered why this was happening, and what else was going on inside the borders of the base.

Falmouth Selectman Virginia Valiela says it came long before she was elected to town office, again in the early 1980s. She is not the sort of person who often trespasses; her heart was pounding, but she snuck onto the military reservation to look at what was happening with the facility's sewage treatment plant. She already suspected the base's sewage had contaminated her town's drinking water. She looked at the filter beds, and she remembers thinking to herself, "They're not going to get away with this."

For Bob Kreykenbohm, manager of the Sandwich Water District, the moment came later, in 1990. Water pumped from deep underground, below what looked like a pristine forest, foamed as it came to the surface. There was enough fuel coming out of the pipe to make a lit match flame. It didn't take long for him to suspect that the only thing that could have caused something so big, so disastrous, was the old pipeline that carried fuel through his town, from Cape Cod Canal to the base.

James Kinney, from Mashpee, remembers the moment he picked up the local newspaper and glanced at one of the headlines. It said that the ponds he loved to fish, the Mashpee ponds which attracted him to Cape Cod, could be contaminated by an invisible threat created decades earlier, by people he'd never met, dumping hazardous waste with names he would only later learn to pronounce.

For Ralph Marks, who now runs the Bourne Water District, the moment came as he pulled the plug and stopped Falmouth's public supply well from pumping water in the late 1970s. Even back then, he figured he knew where the contamination was coming from. It was coming from the same place where he had been serving his National Guard duty as a "weekend warrior."

Susan Nickerson, executive director of the Association for the Preservation of Cape Cod, remembers the day in 1985 when she buttonholed the deputy director of the Environmental Protection Agency in this region. She worked for the county's public planning commission back then; she believed (and still believes) in the regulatory process. But this EPA official had shown up on Cape Cod to announce that no environmental impact statement would be needed before further building moved forward on the huge military reservation. Just before the press conference, she pulled him aside to ask if he knew that a second drinking well had just been shut down, contaminated by underground pollution created on the base. On the spot, the EPA changed its position, and demanded serious study before more military development could proceed. It was a political "victory," a first step.

Richard Hugus, who moved to Falmouth from Minneapolis hoping to build boats and enjoy a cleaner, quieter place to live, remembers the moment in 1991 when he stopped in at a meeting of a citizens group called Alliance for Base Cleanup. He had thought there were people taking care of the problem, people on top of the issue. He looked around, and saw a small group who "desperately needed help."

For Denis LeBlanc, who studies geology and underground water movement, the moment came more than 15 years ago, when he sank a test well into the sandy soil on the southern side of the base. As it turned out, he had put his first dart into the bullseye: thousands of test wells and samples later, the Ashumet Valley plume would become studied, analyzed, and charted with more detail than virtually any other plume in the country.

Susan Walker from Sandwich still shakes her head thinking about her moment, in 1981. Her daughter was in kindergarten, and a schoolmate brought a small egg-shaped object to show and tell, a little thing he had picked up in the woods. It was a live artillery shell from the base. If it had gone off, the kill radius was 15 feet. Military personnel said it was the responsibility of parents to keep their children out of the woods; Walker began the months of lobbying it would take to convince the base to build fences around its property.

George Seaver's moment came in 1993. He was looking out his window in Cataumet, a village of Bourne, observing a strange activity: a monitoring well was being installed smack in the middle of his neighborhood. Monitoring for what? he asked. Oh, a plume is crossing under Route 28, he was told. It's moving a foot or two per day, so we need to find out if it has reached here yet.

For Terry White, who grew up hanging around the base with his dad, who dove in the local ponds every chance he got, who served in the Coast Guard, it was the moment he was told he had an unusual lymphoma—different than the rare brain tumor which killed his father, but life-threatening just the same. He'd never be able to prove it in court, but there was no doubt in his mind about where and when both he and his father had been exposed to carcinogens.

"There have been natural tensions that existed over a period of time," Senator Kennedy acknowledged as he sat in the hot summer sun on July 7, 1994. "But these differences have been put aside. . . to ensure the health and safety and well being of our families."

"There have been frustrations," Senator Kerry added, "agonies, and anxieties."

Standing to one side of the ceremony, looking a bit anxious, Dan Santos kept himself out of the limelight. Since 1990 he had been in charge of the cleanup at the base, a civilian point man for a military hierarchy. He had taken heat every which way. There were the green shirts (the Army) and the blue shirts (the Air Force) who didn't see eye to eye. There was a state chain of command that led to the Adjutant General's office in Reading, Massachusetts, and a federal chain of command that led to the Pentagon in Washington. Some of the brass thought he wasn't a team player, said he was allowing too much involvement from these activist/radical types who really wanted nothing but to shut the base down. Some of the public thought he was a smoother version of the Old Guard, covering up and co-opting, a yes-man for the Defense Department, manipulative and not committed to real democratic process.

Pulled in many directions for a long time, walking a fine line for years, this moment was a quiet satisfaction for Dan Santos, if not a vindication. Within a month he would announce his plans to leave the public sector, to get into engineering and consulting, away from the burn of public scrutiny. Personally, this was a culminating moment, but professionally it was only the beginning of the real work he had been hired to do; someone else would have to manage the effort to try to stop these plumes.

"You have become a family," Congressman Studds was concluding. "You have amassed names and acronyms for what you are trying to accomplish that are beyond the ken of anyone outside your family."

"This is wild," whispered Mark Forest, head of Studds' Cape Cod office, who had plugged away on this plan for years. "I needed to be here myself just to make sure it's really true."

With a quarter of a billion dollars apparently committed to building and operating a giant pollution treatment plant, this will likely be the biggest public works project on Cape Cod since they dug the canal—on second thought, since a stretch of fields and scrub pine forest was turned into a city called Camp Edwards, which housed 50,000 soldiers as World War II approached.

This also happens to be the most ambitious military base cleanup in the entire country so far. Everything about it, the political process, the way money is spent (and has been wasted), the technology used, will influence how other military facilities around the country handle similar problems.

The precedent is no abstract, armchair matter. Latest reports indicate that nearly 1000 military installations in our nation already have been identified as harboring more than 10,000 sites of environmental pollution. U.S. bases overseas, from Germany to the Philippines, also have scary problems. Unfortunately, the list can only grow as investigation moves forward. It is possible that one more may turn out to be in Cape Cod's backyard: the North

7

Truro Air Force Base.

And so Cape Cod finds itself in the vanguard of what will be one of the most important environmental issues to face this country as we move into the next century. This peninsula arrived here first for a number of reasons: the sandy soil allowed pollution to move very far, very fast, off the base. The communities in the area are close by and sophisticated; people have come to understand that Cape Cod's groundwater is crucial and irreplaceable. And in these neighborhoods are people with substantial resources, scientific and financial, which can be brought to bear to confront big issues, and big bureaucracies.

So the story of this place on the Upper Cape which goes by many names—the Massachusetts Military Reservation, Cape Cod's military base, Camp Edwards, Otis Air Force Base—is a fascinating tale in its own right, with Shakespearean characters and themes. But like all good theater, it rises to another level. The drama will be played over and over again, wherever military facilities offer a stage, because it debuts a national theme:

We face a threat left behind by a generation which did not fully realize what it had done, which was worried about dangers from abroad rather than dangers of our own making. Blame no longer matters as much as responsibility, and results. Denial, distrust, turf battles, hidden agendas, foot dragging, and corporate waste can paralyze the process. Courage, consensus, good faith, and a stubbornly active community can force action.

Each generation's challenge is to learn from the past. Today, the lesson which must be learned is that the environment should never be sacrificed for what seems at the moment to be compelling reasons—like fighting the Red Menace, or even something more mundane, like paving the way for careless economic development.

And for the military, who have emerged in the strange dual role as strongest protector and biggest polluter, the challenge can be put more simply: the time has come to embrace the idea that the definition of national security now includes environmental protection. Their mission is to create a new kind of security: natural security.

If Cape Cod offers insight into how people make that happen, how to avoid delay and defeat, then whatever local success has been achieved will be multiplied. And this would be fitting; this would add to a long pattern. Because from the very beginning nearly a century ago, this chunk of land at the northeast corner of the country, in the thickest part of a tiny peninsula, has had an uncanny knack of capturing and symbolizing a huge nation's experience:

It began as a sheep ranch, it became a Superfund hazardous waste site, and in between it carried us into war and patrolled our border in peace. It has been used to aim artillery and assault beaches, to practice infantry locksteps as well as bombing runs, to imprison German prisoners of war as well as American defectors, to direct radar surveillance and even house poised atomic weapons. Generation by generation, incarnation by incarnation, this one base has acted out the priorities, and expressed the attitude, of that complex thing called the American military.

2

THE BEGINNING, AND THE EXPLOSION

Environmental protection was on no one's mind in 1911, but other forms of protection were.

The Massachusetts National Guard—the modern version of Minutemen, who with a minute's notice could leave their plows and pick up their muskets to face the British—had come to the conclusion that even part-time troops needed to be a bit more sophisticated to be effective. Muskets didn't cut it in the 20th century. The Guard wanted to be able to practice with "live" ammunition in its cannons and rifles.

The various armories the Guard owned around the state couldn't provide sufficient space for such blasting at a distance. For units located around Boston, New Bedford, and Fall River, the open expanse of what was the Shawme-Crowell State Forest in Sandwich seemed like an ideal range. Training began in the fall of 1911, in what is now the northern part of the base, in what is still generally referred to as "the Impact Area."

This was a remote part of the world back then, no neighbors to complain about noise and smoke two weeks a year. Then again, it may have been that those gangs of workmen a few miles west, with their dredges banging into rock and muck every day and night, were making so much noise that they drowned out the artillery. They'd started in 1909, and still had three years to go before they'd be done digging the Cape Cod Canal. A local poet at the time was moved to pen one of the Cape's earliest anti-development protests, which he called the "Buzzards Bay Dredging Dirge:"

Oh, Please go 'way and let us sleep,
You dredgers there make din so deep
That day or night we lose our rest,
Our bliss you blight—You're sure a pest—
So please go 'way and let us sleep.

When the Massachusetts National Guard went away in 1917, the soldiers' work had only begun. Their cannon and rifle training was eerily timed: there was no way for them to know that they would soon become the 26th Infantry Division, and see bitter combat during World War I, much of it over the course of 10 months in France. They became famous as the "Yankee Division," and the so-called "Daddy of the Division" was a popular major general by the name of Clarence R. Edwards. When Edwards died in Boston in 1931, thousands of people filed past his coffin at the Hall of Flags in the State House. Only a few years later, the training camp on Cape Cod would bear his name.

But at the war's end that camp did not yet exist. For years, there was talk about trying to consolidate Shawme-Crowell holdings with private land directly south of the state forest, and create an area big enough for an entire division of soldiers to live and train. Much of that private land in the heart of the Cape had been divided into long, skinny woodlots generations earlier, the old hardwood trees harvested (and ravaged by forest fires) to such an extent that the flat plateau of land had become covered mainly by scrawny pines and oak.

In 1920, a private group of investors from New York beat the military to the punch, buying roughly 14,000 acres spanning Bourne, Falmouth, Mashpee, and Sandwich. The Coonamessett Ranch Company, as they called themselves, seemed intent on creating what was described as "the largest sheep ranch east of the Mississippi," but the ranch was more hype than fact. There was some tourist development on the Falmouth side of the property, a golf course and an inn, but the scrub was not much disturbed. Even when the group sold out to Charles R. Crane in 1930, who used some of the millions he had made producing plumbing fixtures to invest in land, the huge tract retained its personality as a Cape Cod version of frontier. Pines remained

11

more common than sheep.

The National Guard and the Commonwealth got serious about creating a huge military base in 1933, and signed an option with Crane to buy 9000 acres of his "ranch," as well as other smaller parcels nearby, like the Lombard Farm beside Sandwich's Snake Pond. Reportedly the government was offering less than $3 per acre for purchase, which even in that era was considered a lowball figure.

But the real controversy was whether such a military presence belonged on Cape Cod at all. According to reports in *The Falmouth Enterprise,* the Cape Cod Chamber of Commerce not only already was in existence, but lobbied against creation of the base. Tourism would be damaged, they argued. A poll of the Chamber's members found 268 opposed to the plan, 111 in favor. When the Chamber conducted a straw vote among summer residents, it found 1368 opposed, 149 in favor.

In February, 1934, citizens gathered at Bourne town hall to discuss the idea. The state's top military officials showed up to explain the advantage of creating a National Guard training camp, and to make a series of promises.

One advantage was economic; more than $2 million would be invested right off the bat to build barracks and warehouses, lay a large airstrip, and all that would mean jobs and boom time. What's more, the artillery training would not bother neighboring towns because "the largest guns to be used there will be three-inch guns and not heavy artillery at all," as *The Wareham Courier* reported. Meanwhile, the area of the reservation "would be beautified in various ways, containing among other things bridle paths, and would be open at all times to the public except for the two weeks or possibly four weeks when the soldiers were here."

Opponents included the Bourne selectmen, the local chamber of commerce, and many of the town's leading lights. They countered that taking all this land out of private hands, 20 square miles of it in Bourne, "some time in the distant future might retard the growth of the town." Summer visitors might be scared off by the base and the artillery firing. The final fear was that "in time of war the federal government might step in and take the camp for an army garrison."

Perhaps the military's arguments were persuasive, or perhaps the perspectives of the towns were different. Regardless, Falmouth town meeting of 1935 took exactly the opposite position, "heartily approving" the base location by a vote of 464 to 94.

Apparently, Falmouth and the military carried more weight than Bourne. $100,000 was appropriated by the state legislature to purchase land for the Guard, the bill signed into law by Massachusetts Governor James Michael Curley in April, 1935. By September, the War Department in Washington had approved the Cape Cod site. By the end of the year, the state's military hierarchy came into proud ownership of 34 square miles of Cape Cod, more than 22,000 acres, about one-tenth of the entire peninsula.

Within a year, the base became the biggest construction project in the state for the WPA (a federal works program designed to soften the blows of the Depression). As many as 600 people were hired to clear brush, level land for tent slabs, runways, and parade grounds, erect a giant water tank to serve bath houses, and install what probably was the first sewer system on Cape Cod. By 1939 the Massachusetts Military Reservation, as the area came to be called, was formally dedicated with nearly 8000 soldiers of the Yankee Division bivouaced for summer training.

There was an urgency building around all this military activity, a growing sense that sooner or later the United States would be drawn into the war overseas.

"Even in America, with the great oceans between us and the worst of it," wrote the great American writer John Dos Passos late in 1940, "we can feel across our windows as we write a shadow of barbed wire."

Dos Passos could well have written those words from one of his haunts at the tip of Cape Cod, in Truro or Provincetown. He certainly would have known that the federal government had responded to that shadow of barbed wire by federalizing the military reservation at the other end of the peninsula, across the bay from him (exactly what some people in Bourne had feared might happen). Once again, as at the beginning of World War I, the Cape was at the leading edge of preparation for the turmoil headed this way.

In September, 1940, less than a week after the federal government officially leased the site, builders and architects already were in place to oversee one of the biggest military construction projects ever undertaken to that time. A defunct sheep ranch was about to become a city.

The magnitude of what was accomplished at the military reservation over the course of a few months remains, to this day, difficult to grasp. In many ways it was one of the earliest examples of how the United States would respond throughout the war years. There was a zeal to get it done, get it done now, don't worry about the cost. This mobilization, a flex of production muscle never seen before, was as important as the bravery of troops overseas in winning World War II.

A construction company headed by a well-known contractor of the time, Thomas Walsh, was put in charge of the push. Walsh had plenty of experience with big projects, having worked on the Grand Coulee dam and New York's mid-town tunnel to Queens. His contract stated that he had 75 days to build 1200 buildings. He announced that 40 million board feet of lumber were about to arrive, which meant he needed 5000 carpenters, immediately. It was a siren call; in one day in October, 1000 men were hired. By November, more than 18,000 people were working on the base. The weekly payroll approached $1 million; these were 1940 dollars, with buying power far beyond our dollars today. Virtually anyone who could move was hired—provided they paid the $75 union membership initiation. Carpenters were making about $1.75 an hour, with time and a half for overtime and double time for Sundays and holidays. For people who had been mired in the Depression, this was a form of manna.

Clark Craig was hired to pound nails at the base, and chronicled his experience for *Harpers Magazine* in March, 1941. His informal survey of hired "carpenters" found "a former clergyman, a lawyer, former clerks in grocery and dime stores, a butcher, a soda jerker, a jeweler, two cooks, a policeman, a soldier, a barber, an undertaker's assistant, and dozens of Cape fishermen."

Earl Mills, born and raised in Mashpee, who would become Chief of the Mashpee Wampanoags in 1957, remembers a neighbor who had moved to town from Roxbury who "didn't know a nail from a hammer. And he was making unbelievable money then, as a carpenter. He learned at the expense of the government. My father would say, 'He has the best tools but he doesn't know what to do with them.'"

Even the famous journalist Walter Winchell became confused by the din. In November of 1940, he reported suspected sabotage (presumably by foreign agents) of the base construction; it turned out to be nothing more than one of the "carpenters" hammering nails into an electric cable and blowing fuses.

"Probably never in the history of the ancient and honorable profession of carpentry have so many sins of omission and commission been done in its name," Craig wrote in his magazine piece. "To frugal-minded Cape Codders there seemed to be only one significant difference between trucks bound for the scrap piles and those arriving from the supply sources—the direction in which they were going."

But efficiency was not the point, just as environmental protection would not be the point for decades to come. There was a threat on our horizon, and speed was of the essence. If anyone at that time had questioned something as mundane as the amount of wasted lumber, he would have been considered either loony, or some sort of foreign dupe.

Meanwhile, the neighboring towns, Falmouth in particular, were booming like never in their histories. Five restaurants in Falmouth were cranking out 1400 meals a day, mostly dinners for workmen who fought through an hour-long traffic jam to make the short trip from the base to downtown. The average check was 50 cents, while these same boarders were paying around $4 a week for lodging. Best estimates said that 2400 people were sleeping temporarily in Falmouth alone. Many locals had turned at least one room of the homestead into guest quarters; others had moved the entire family into the basement, the better to cash in on the bonanza.

The flood of money from the base was easily recognized, because workers were paid in new $20 bills—three per week for a typical laborer. A local grocer reportedly made change for 27 consecutive $20 bills one payday evening. Such pay was a long way up from "the dole," $11 a week in Depression-era welfare, which too many people had been forced to take in lieu of nothing.

But the mission of the work was not economic revival. It was military preparation. By January, 1941, four months after the first lumber arrived, a post office opened on the reservation. The first air mail stamp was put on a card sent to Franklin Roosevelt at the White House. It read, "Mr. President, Camp Edwards is ready."

The Walsh construction effort resulted in almost 1400 buildings (more than originally contracted, many identical wood-framed barracks) using 12.7 million square feet of roofing and sheathing paper, 3.9 million square feet of wall board, and 3500 porcelain washbasins. Crews laid a new railroad spur nearly nine miles long from Sagamore onto the base. There were 40 miles of water mains feeding three 150-foot-tall water towers, 34 miles of sewer mains to deal with 700,000 gallons daily. About 30 miles of road was carved. A large landfill (known in those days as the dump) was centrally located and received anything and everything that had no more use. Ballfields, movie theaters, and a large convalescent hospital all soon rose up on the Cape Cod plains.

"There were 12 or 13 chapels in Camp Edwards, Catholic, Protestant, and Jewish," remembers Robert Phelan, who served there in the 1940s and has gathered a great deal of historical information about the base now that he lives in Falmouth. "That's how big the place was."

Thomas Walsh originally was budgeted $7.2 million to build the military reservation (of which he got to keep 3.22 percent). By January, 1941, the total construction cost was $29 million, and climbing. Within a few more years, adding in work done at satellite facilities, the cost approached $50 million. Walsh certainly didn't suffer from the overruns, moving on to build bases in the Caribbean, as well as ships for the Navy. He was the first of many contractors to make hefty paychecks, even small fortunes, from work at the base.

The Yankee Division was one of 10 National Guard groups around the country inducted into federal service, then exposed to months of intense training. Through the year of 1941 that training took place in and around Camp Edwards, as thousands of men worked on everything from handling grenades to marching in step.

Aerial work also began immediately. The airfield, named after a pilot from the National Guard named Dr. Frank Jesse Otis who had died in a crash in 1937, was gearing up for the kind of work it would host for decades to come: surveillance.

Lester Tipping, now in his 80s, remembers being among "the first airplanes in here. It was early 1941. We hand cranked all our planes (to get them started)." Tipping was an engineer, one of four men per plane who remained airborne for eight hours at a time. "We were looking for German submarines. We'd pinpoint where they were, and call the Navy. They'd send out a destroyer, and try to sink them." These submarines had been harassing Cape Cod fishing boats and other commercial carriers.

The infantry kept to solid land. Training had finished in early December, 1941, after a series of maneuvers in the Carolinas. A large number of men was standing at attention at the base parade grounds as a sergeant came forward with papers in hand, authorizing him to send them on the long-awaited trip home in time for Christmas. Without warning, there was a delay. The sergeant went back into headquarters. When he returned, he was tearing up those papers. It was December 7. The Japanese had attacked Pearl Harbor. Instead of going home, many of those troops soon found themselves on their way to Australia, transported on cattle barges to join in the Battle of Coral Sea and the Guadalcanal invasion. They became part of the Americal Division.

The need for soldiers was nearly insatiable. Within months, 50,000 people were assigned to Camp Edwards, overflowing barracks built to handle about

30,000. Some were bivouaced in Plymouth at Camp Miles Standish. Others slept at Camp Wellfleet, near what is now the Marconi site of the Cape Cod National Seashore. Despite the crush, housing on the base remained segregated; "Negro" soldiers not only slept apart, but socialized at their own USO hall in Mashpee. "It was just about the only place where they'd allow black people in," remembers Earl Mills.

The size and location of Camp Edwards made it ideal for a number of unique training missions. Most visible were anti-aircraft schools set up on Scorton Neck in Sandwich, and along the high dunes of Wellfleet; combined, they became the largest anti-aircraft training base in the United States. Big guns mounted on swiveling platforms lined the shores, with smaller machine guns alongside. Planes dragged 30-foot white sleeves, which were the targets, as far behind them as they could get. Day and night, explosions and fireworks burst over the water, and for years after, finding munition shells along the beaches was nearly as easy as finding seashells.

Noman's Island off Martha's Vineyard became another target, this time for bombers practicing their drops. But the most important use of the beaches was as training for amphibious assaults. This was the first and biggest site for this work, and the men here became part of what was called the Engineer Amphibian Command. Training with plywood boats, using makeshift facilities known as Camp Have Done It (in Osterville), Camp Can't Do It (in Cotuit), and Washburn's Island (which had been occupied by the military), the "Cape Cod Commandoes" worked the shores so hard that they were blamed for destroying Cotuit's fertile oyster beds, and closing the mouth of Falmouth Harbor by sucking too much sand into the entrance.

No such complaints stopped the training. The idea was to get troops ready for the kinds of invasions carried out across the Pacific, in Africa, and for the most famous of all, D-Day at Normandy—where weather and terrain very much resembled what was found on Nantucket Sound.

As a final exercise, the amphibians would launch "top secret" mock invasions. The handy spot to invade was across the Sound from Falmouth, to occupy that hotbed of enemy activity known as Martha's Vineyard. Although the flotillas left under cover of darkness and arrived at daybreak, somehow islanders seemed to get wind that they were about to be invaded, and would line the beaches in anticipation. An article printed by *The Falmouth Enterprise* in 1942 (and cleared by military censors) described the "invasion:"

> **While wave after wave of amphibious infantrymen stormed the island at three different points, parachute troops swooped down, seized the vital enemy-held airport at Edgartown and assisted the invaders in establishing a grip on the island. Once the invasion got underway there was no halting of the terrific onrush of the infantrymen, who, after debarking from their craft, charged forward to contact the enemy in face of withering machinegun fire and ceaseless bombing from enemy aircraft.**

Even during this most patriotic and single-minded time, not all Americans were ready and willing to head overseas and fight for liberty. Those from east of the Mississippi who were caught trying to "jump ship" and escape service found themselves at Camp Edwards in the East Coast Processing Center, one of only two such centers in the country. As many as 45,000 men passed through this center, where a combination of threats and therapy was used to try to get them on the boats for battle. Psychiatrists and MPs both got into the act, although according to one eyewitness named Howard Welestio, who wrote this account years later, there was more muscle than mind involved:

> **These inmates were sort of bad. Most post personnel... were under orders to stay away due to the fact that these birds would assault anyone verbally, physically (rocks, refuse, etc) to get court-martialed and jailed and thus remain in the U.S. at any cost and not be cannon fodder overseas. They were heavily guarded. Each one has his own personal MP with a fixed bayonet at all times until placed aboard a troopship.**

At the other end of the spectrum, Camp Edwards soon housed several thousand German prisoners of war, mainly captured from Rommel's units in North Africa. Most of the time they worked on the base itself, although the prisoners also were used to do agricultural work like cranberry picking. It must have amazed them to see that the Americans had built a mock German village in the camp, a kind of Hollywood set complete with swastikas and signs in German announcing a "biergarten" and other businesses, all presumably to help train for an occupation.

Locals did not seem to be much scared of these POWs, except perhaps in an economic way:

"Every American soldier in the bake shops, service and repair jobs, at Edwards is a potential customer of Falmouth," wrote *The Falmouth Enterprise* in 1944. "Nazis who take over these jobs and free American soldiers for other assignments are not. Both the prisoners of war and East Coast Processing Center stockades represent camp population which can't visit us."

After the war, some of these German prisoners extended their visits, preferring to stay rather than return to a Europe in turmoil. They began their lives again as Cape Cod residents.

Despite *The Enterprise's* complaint, the base created tremendous economic opportunity, providing both jobs and customers. Even teenagers like Earl Mills would work fixing trucks, or selling newspapers barracks to barracks. Off-duty soldiers might rent boats for a dollar and fish in local ponds by day, then frequent hopping bars like Jake's in East Falmouth, the Blue Parrot in Cataumet, the Domino Club in Buzzards Bay, and Peter's Pond Club in Mashpee. In short, the Depression was over.

On the base, the movement of people and material was staggering. A group like the 82nd Airborne, 18,000 soldiers, might spend as little as 10 days at the camp and then move out—but not before a brawl broke out between the 82nd and the amphibian engineers over who had the right to wear paratrooper boots. A division from Texas spent six months in training—and local nightclubs banned the singing of "Eyes of Texas" because it somehow seemed to introduce too many fights. The Women's Auxiliary Army Corps slept for a week in tents in the Mashpee woods, and participated in training similar to combat units, before leaving to serve as nurses and support staff wherever the war was joined overseas.

And the tide of people through the base flowed both ways. One of the largest Army hospitals in the country was receiving hundreds of wounded soldiers. Special hospital trains carried patients along the new spur to every part of the country; in one week almost 4000 men were moved. Hospital staff handled 2500 people at a time, and specialized in prosthetics. A swimming pool was installed to help rehabilitation. Some of the wounded soldiers were returned to the front, but most went home. Twenty years later a young Jacqueline Kennedy would go into labor unexpectedly while in Hyannis, and deliver a son (who did not survive infancy) at the same hospital.

Camp Edwards was created to prepare and respond to war. By 1946, that mission had been completed. The base immediately changed status, becoming "inactive" by military description. But this did not mean that 34 square miles of Cape Cod was returned to civilian control. Instead, this was the first of a number of periods when the base seemed to fall mostly dormant, rousing when the National Guard's "weekend warriors" arrived for training.

At the time, people wondered whether the base would ever see such intense activity again. To this day it has not. Yet the reservation would soon become an integral part of the nation's military machinery once again.

Yes, World War II had been won. But The War To End All Wars was not that. A much longer conflict was soon joined, in which Cape Cod served as a sentry and outpost. This war came to be known by a strange adjective: Cold.

3

THE COLD WAR YEARS

Immediately after the war, the Army turned control of the entire base over to the Air Force. The reservation became known as Otis Air Force Base (a name which clings to this day even though it is not strictly accurate—the facility dwarfs what remains of the air base). It was a time of transition, a time to take stock. Public officials decided they needed a master plan for the area; they wanted to know what all the war buildup had left behind.

The plan was delivered in 1950, and soon became one of those documents tucked away in a forgotten folder, which only now clangs with the irony of hindsight:

Details of the camp showed 31 gas stations, four fire stations, five service clubs, three libraries, nine diamonds for baseball and softball, 12 outdoor basketball courts, one hospital—the list goes on. Also inventoried were four gravel-wall wells, each 90 feet deep, as well as six 10,000-gallon tanks used for jet fuel. Even then, there was a blunt assessment about problems that are haunting us today: "The drainage facilities for Camp Edwards are inadequate."

The plan didn't recommend much in the way of remedies, just noted the fact. And in comments about the base's coal storage area, which could handle 125,000 tons to feed the power plants, a clearer sense emerges of where environmental concerns fit in at that time:

"Only a small portion of the coal storage area is presently paved. With the expense and amount of work involved, it is questionable whether this area should even be paved. The amount of coal lost because of the absence of paving is but a fraction of what it would cost to pave the entire area."

The pavement that soon became of paramount concern was found on the runways. Each ribbon was thousands of feet long, and happened to be laid down at the edge of the continent, one of the closest places in America to Europe. Otis Air Force Base, as people would soon think of the entire reservation, assumed key strategic importance in military thinking. Guard training at Camp Edwards continued, particularly as the United States geared up once more to fight in Korea. But the air side of the base became crucial, because the Cold War was turning into a high-stakes game of surveillance, with both Russian and US planes constantly probing each other's defenses and perimeters.

By 1955, Otis Airfield became headquarters for one of two squadrons in the country (the other was in California) which flew what were known as the "Connies," superconstellation reconnaissance aircraft easily identified by their distinctive triple-humped tails. There were variations on the theme—C-121s, RC-121s and EC-121s—but the idea was always the same: these planes were flying radar stations, kept aloft with the help of giant tanks of fuel which made their wings droop as they taxied for takeoff. Each wing tank could hold 600 gallons, which meant that once a Connie was airborne, it could stay up for 16 hours, covering 5400 miles with four engines running. One flight loop might take the crew toward Newfoundland and back; another toward Florida and back.

"We started with three aircraft and slowly built them up," remembers Walden Bock, who served at Otis from 1955 until 1970, when he retired as chief master sergeant. The planes would arrive from the West Coast, while crews went through training exercises. Before long, there were more than 40 Connies stationed on the Cape.

"We were flying 24 hours a day, seven days a week," remembers Mel Miller, a retired tech sergeant who worked the flight lines. "That was the big push, boy: no holes in the flight coverage. Keep that next plane coming." When all was going according to plan, planes were lifting off every four hours.

The pressure was on; we needed a blanket of radar surveillance so the Russians wouldn't be able to pull off a sneak attack. Operational readiness,

22

OR, was the buzzphrase. And there was only one maintenance hangar out there, now known as Building 158, which could handle no more than four planes at a time. Space was at a premium, but repairs were constant.

For instance, there were a lot of hydraulics on these big planes. A landing gear strut, 10 inches in diameter, might hold four gallons or more of hydraulic fluid. Very often, the seals on these struts would go bad and leak, especially in winter when they froze and lost their elasticity. They had to be replaced before a plane could take off and land safely.

"You'd pull a plug out of the bottom (of the strut), put in new seals, get it back together, and get the plane out," Miller remembers. "Then you'd hose it (the floor) down, and everything went down the drain. Hundreds and hundreds of gallons of hydraulic fluid went down the drain. I have no idea where the drain went."

Meanwhile, Connies laden with fuel were safe for takeoff, but if for some reason they needed to land quickly (say if there was an engine failure), the huge tanks had to be emptied. Otherwise, the plane might blow up. Built into the design were four chutes, hydraulically activated valves which would lighten the load by dumping hundreds of gallons of fuel per minute. At the end of the runway there was a test area, basically just a stretch of flat ground which drained away from the runway. Periodically, the planes would taxi over there and have their valves checked, a routine maintenance sort of thing. It didn't happen every time a Connie flew (which later was alleged), but it did happen regularly, and each time hundreds of gallons of fuel were sent seeping into the ground.

"Where did the fuel go from there?" asks Miller. "I never questioned it."

Richard Kolbert, a flight engineer on the Connies who flew from 1957 until 1968, also remembers dumping hydraulic fluid all the time. There were red cans, five gallon and 10, as well as barrels of it. "I wanted uncontaminated fluid in my planes," he recalls. "Any thought of it being contaminated, I wouldn't want it in my aircraft." Often it went into the landfill. Kolbert describes the common attitude as "Hey, dump it in the ground, that's it. By the case, I used to get rid of it."

As flight engineer, Kolbert's airborne responsibilities included making safety decisions. "If I blew an engine shortly after takeoff, I wasn't concerned about dumping fuel to save our asses," he explains. "I'm the one who pulled the levers and said, 'We're dumping.'"

Lester Tipping, one of the first to fly in the 1940s, returned to the base during the era of the Connies. "Fuel was taken anywhere and dumped on the base," he remembers. "You'd drain fuel out of the engines to work on them. Contaminated fuel, it was. It would go in barrels and be stored. Where it went wasn't my business, but it went somewhere."

All refueling of the Connies was done on the ground, according to Walden Bock. It would take two big trucks to fill the tanks on one plane. Fuel was cheap, spills were common, and procedures didn't change all that much from the 1950s right through the era of training for Vietnam missions in the 1960s, until the Connies were finally phased out in 1969.

When parts wore out, they needed to be replaced, and discarded. For example, the EC-121s used radioactive electron vacuum tubes in their radar sets. According to reports filed years later, from 1955 through 1970 approximately 200 of these tubes a year were sent to a gravel pit 20 feet square, just north of the landfill. Various types of radioactive isotopes might have been used in these tubes, like cesium-137, tritium, cobalt-60, or radium-226. Some of these have long "half-lives," meaning they remain radioactive for a long time. Others decay very quickly.

One improvement that was made involved the fuel dump valve checks: eventually, caps were installed on the valves, which cut down on the number of gallons lost. What was dumped then "would go into barrels and up to what we called the burning pit, the fire training area," adds Bock. There it would be poured back on the ground (along with most anything else flammable) and burned to give the base firefighters something to practice on. What burned sent up big billows of black smoke; what didn't burn seeped into the dirt.

People had little sense that what they were doing would damage the environment. "Would you have stopped your son from pouring his used motor oil in the woods in 1957?" asks Richard Kolbert. In essence, he argues, that was what was going on at the base, on a huge scale.

But even then, there were concerns among some, questions that were never asked. "You didn't rock the boat," says Mel Miller. "If you questioned anything, you were unofficially labeled as a troublemaker. And they always needed a lot of bodies for a few different unpleasant details, like mess check count, or fire guard at night. . . I used to fish in Ashumet Pond. That's just this side of the fuel tanks. A little ditch runs through the cranberry bog to the pond. You could see oil slicks coming into the pond back then. If you wanted extra detail, hey, just complain."

By 1957, when the Connies were really hitting their stride, the Air Force announced that Cape Cod had been chosen as one of four sites in the northeast (and 16 in the country) to host yet another level of protection from the Soviet threat.

"Air Force will build a $10.7 million missile launching site at Otis," announced *The Falmouth Enterprise* on December 7, 1957. The name of the system was BOMARC, which stood for Boeing Michigan Aeronautical Research Center, where the missile was created.

The BOMARC was designed to stop enemy bombers from penetrating American airspace, a last defense of sorts. A supersonic rocket, using liquid or solid rocket fuel depending on the type, theoretically could track and destroy a bomber as far as 60,000 feet away (although it was considered ineffective against an intercontinental ballistic missile). Each BOMARC was 47 feet long, weighed more than four tons, and would be housed in its own little building, with a roof that scissored open like a domed telescope observatory.

The designers of this defensive weapon, looking to optimize its potential effectiveness, added one key ingredient: the missile would carry a nuclear warhead.

"Small hydrogen bombs are intended primarily as substitutes for the existing small tactical atomic bombs," *The Enterprise* explained, adding a dubious scientific note: "The H- bombs would presumably produce less radioactivity."

The newspaper described a meeting planned for December 13, 1957, between the Air Force and local luminaries, to be held at the Otis Officers' club, to explain what was coming:

"First there will be cocktails, then dinner. . . Suitably relaxed by this hospitality, the guests will then address themselves to the missile."

At the gathering, the BOMARC was described as "an almost unbelievable engineering feat," which could bring atomic force to a far-flung target. The colonel in charge of the briefing referred to the missile as "a one-shot deal." The reporter explained: "When the BOMARC is fired, it will be the real thing and, as one of the panel put it, it will then not matter in quite the same way if a missile misfired and drops its atomic load on Cape Cod." Presumably, what the writer meant was that the Russians would be attacking, so one more "atomic load" wouldn't make all that much difference.

Joseph Sorenti, whose family name was seen atop businesses at the Sagamore rotary for many years, announced what apparently was the general conclusion: "I feel a hell of a lot safer tonight than I did last night."

This type of candid discussion about the BOMARCs stopped as soon as the missiles themselves arrived in 1960. The BOMARC area became super secure; even personnel from the rest of the base were not allowed inside without special clearance.

Meanwhile, one of the other BOMARC sites in the northeast, McGuire Air Force Base in New Jersey, suddenly found itself on the front page of *The New York Times* in June, 1960. One of the missiles caught fire on its launching pad. In the understandable panic, someone called state police to say that "an atomic warhead" had exploded. People evacuated the area.

What actually happened was that the booster part of the missile burned into a molten fireball, with such intensity that the housing around the nuclear bomb melted. Radioactivity spewed all over the launching area, forcing officials to seal it in concrete. The commander of the base, a General Pritchard, assured the public that "contamination was confined within the four walls of the shelter proper, with residue flushing down in the sand fully 1500 feet from the highway." The day following the accident, he was able to add that "wells 600 feet from the site showed no contamination," according to *The Times*.

It was common knowledge in 1960 that BOMARC missiles were nuclear. It also became known fairly quickly that the BOMARCs, with serious flaws in design and execution, were obsolete almost as soon as they were built. As early as March, 1960, the Air Force cut funding for the system because the Soviet Union was shifting from manned bombers to intercontinental missiles—which the BOMARCs could not stop even if they worked properly. Meanwhile, Defense Department engineers were admitting that "serious technical difficulties" made the BOMARC difficult to rely upon.

Despite this history, the Defense Department has resisted efforts to understand the atomic history at Otis. For years, the typical response to all inquiries about these 28 hangars housing two missiles each, located within 600 feet of a residential subdivision, was to "neither confirm nor deny" the presence of atomic weapons on Cape Cod.

"The information is classified until and unless it is declassified," says Cheri Abdelnour from the Defense Nuclear Agency, which reportedly maintains records of nuclear stockpiles.

After months of repeated efforts to break through this Catch 22, efforts supported by inquiries from the Washington office of Congressman Gerry Studds, the Defense Nuclear Agency issued the following statement:

"We are able to confirm that nuclear weapons were formerly present at Otis AFB, MA. However, we cannot confirm the type or quantity of nuclear weapons present, as that information remains classified."

According to the agency, "normal practice" would have been to "ship nuclear warheads and their associated launch or delivery vehicles separately." The bombs (which were produced at the Pantex Plant near Amarillo, Texas) and the rockets would then be assembled on site. The "preferred methods of delivery" of the bombs "are by truck or by cargo aircraft." The agency would not say what type of delivery system was used at Otis.

Such sketchy information is hardly satisfying. Cloaks of secrecy remain in place even though the operation reportedly was dismantled and eliminated in 1973, more than 20 years ago, more than 30 years after it was deemed superfluous for national security.

We do know that the BOMARC area (which had once been a rifle range) was completely self-contained, a little city within a little city, with its own powerplant, fire station, missile maintenance and testing buildings, fueling and defueling sites. Liquid fuel, which is extremely volatile and dangerous, was made up of red fuming nitric acid as an oxidizer, and aerozine-50 as fuel; contact with air would cause explosions (as people found out in New Jersey), so everything had to be handled with care. Solid rocket fuel was introduced later, which was safer to handle but environmentally even more dangerous, because it didn't volatize as easily and so sank into the ground. Seven underground tanks held several different types of fuel used for engine and rocket power, such as hydrazine, JP4, and MOGAS. One leaching well was dug to catch spills from these tanks, while another pit caught the nitric acid after it was passed through limestone to stop the violent reaction; both seeped directly into the ground. One of the many buildings (known as #4633) was "used for warhead storage."

Fred Turkington, well known in his hometown of Falmouth, was a lieutenant colonel and an Air Force Intelligence Officer at that time. As such, he had clearance into the BOMARC site, and visited it several times.

"It was always hush-hush about the fact that there were atomic-tipped missiles there," he recalls. "(But) it was very informal. Nobody ever sat down and said, 'You got to know this and don't mention it.' . . . Everyone just assumed the BOMARC missile was atomic." When it came to storage, as well as "the messy job of moving things on and off the base," Turkington recalls that "great precautions were used in that regard."

Unfortunately, as we would learn later, such care was not exercised in many other parts of the secret facility.

The architect and engineer for the BOMARC site was a Boston firm who, according to *The Falmouth Enterprise,* had been hired by the military to design another of the sophisticated, advanced early warning systems deemed necessary in those years, and controlled from Otis: The "Texas Towers."

The nickname came from the fact that these stationary platforms were built far out to sea, along George's Bank, patterned on oil drilling rigs used in the Gulf of Mexico. Once again, radar surveillance at the far edge of our national boundaries, and what the Air Force called "weapon directing capability," were the reasons the towers were considered vital to national security.

All three of these towers, built in the late 1950s, were manned by crews from Otis. 75 people usually were stationed on each platform, held above the waves by three huge legs with their concrete feet on the ocean floor.

One of the platforms, located about 65 miles off the New Jersey coast, had been nicknamed "Old Shaky" because it swayed so much. After Hurricane Donna battered the tower in September of 1960, most of the men were removed, leaving 14 radar specialists and 14 civilian repairmen, "many of whom were fearful of living on the shaking structure," as an account in *The Cape Cod Times* reported. In part because of their urgings, the station was going to be evacuated as early as daylight on Monday, January 16, 1961, but no later than the end of the month.

Tragically, that plan could not be carried out. On the night of January 15, the tower collapsed. All 28 men on board were killed in the worst peacetime accident to hit personnel from the base.

The commanding officer at the time, Colonel Ernest White, called a press conference several days later to "try to stop some of the completely garbled stuff that has been appearing" about the tragedy. He said that "all troubles on Tower 4 had been squared away by August 6," but the hurricane in September "gave us some trouble." The drowned men, Colonel White said, "were doing their job. . . Danger is our business. In some instances we have to take risks in the best interests of the United States."

Meanwhile, a very different type of risk had been proposed for the military reservation itself. Early in 1960, Cape Codders got wind of a piece of legislation moving through the State House in Boston which would have established a "nuclear park" at Camp Edwards.

The bill was the result of hearings and reports from the Massachusetts Atomic Energy Commission (among others), and would have allowed virtually every type of nuclear activity: processing spent fuel rods from nuclear reactors, building a nuclear power plant, and installing underground storage tanks for high-level radioactive waste.

"There is much to commend this site," reported the state commission, "like sparse population in the immediate area. . ."

Among the "sparse" group of people in the area were some of the most eminent scientists and researchers in the world, working out of Woods Hole. Dr. Arthur Redfield, by that time retired as director of the Oceanographic Institution, was joined by the likes of Dr. Albert Szent-Gyorgyl, a Nobel prizewinner for medicine, and many other colleagues who brought withering arguments against the idea.

"We are living, so to speak, over a lake into which those iron tanks holding atomic waste have to be lowered. . . If one of those tanks becomes leaky, or cracks. . . then there will be no power on earth to prevent the atomic waste from spreading and getting into our drinking water and we can wipe Cape Cod off the map as a place fit for human habitation," wrote Dr. Szent-Gyorgyl.

Dr. Redfield produced an extraordinary map which showed Cape Cod's water table, indicating that underground water flowed from the military base toward the shorelines. The map, although crude, is very similar to modern maps which guide cleanup work to this day.

Given this geography, any kind of accident on the site would send radioactive material through the sand and into the Cape's water supply, Redfield explained. "It might be years before it reached our wells," he continued. "But tourists would sure to be unhappy."

Various Chambers of Commerce, on the other hand, strongly supported the nuclear park concept. Henry Roberti, president of the Buzzards Bay Chamber, felt that "actually, these alarmists cannot raise a single factual objection to this legislation which will benefit not only the Cape, but every person in the Free World in this space age."

The president of the Cape Cod Chamber, Floyd Van Duzer, accused the scientists of "a very good scare job," and went so far as to invoke Joseph McCarthy: "There are some Communists on the Cape," he said, "and there are some sympathizers."

But the alarm had been sounded. When public hearings on the proposal were held, halls were packed with opposition. Various state politicians saw which way the gale was blowing, and killed the bill. Cape Cod was spared the fate of those places that would become some of the most dangerously polluted areas on the planet.

In hindsight, the deep irony of the situation is obvious: at the very moment these scientists were mobilizing against what they saw as a radioactive threat, pollution of another kind already was pouring from the base, and would move underground in exactly the manner they had predicted.

By 1965, the base had a new way of receiving much of the fuel it needed to keep its equipment moving: a pipeline was built from Cape Cod Canal to the reservation. A storage farm in Sandwich fed a three-inch pipe which ran up Tupper Road, along Grove Street, crossed under Route 6, and followed Greenway Road south onto base property. Standard Transmission Corporation, based in Cushing, Oklahoma, was responsible for the line, which ran more than seven miles.

According to Evan J. Albright, editor of *The Register* newspaper, Standard Transmission worked out a series of agreements with town and state officials, railroad interests, and the US Army Corps of Engineers, which created the necessary easements to build and bury the pipe. The company stood to make as much as 10 cents per barrel on fuel delivered, "a potential gold mine," as Albright puts it, except that there were so many easements and right-of-ways to be bought that the profits were drastically reduced.

Bob Kreykenbohm, who manages the Sandwich Water District, remembers how the system used to work: the man responsible for the big tanks along the canal would get a call, telling him the base needed fuel. "He used to flip the switch," says Kreykenbohm, "and then go to the old Dan'l Webster Inn for lunch. About four hours later he'd go back—that was about how long it took for the fuel to arrive." It was a casual process, he adds, because back then fuel was "cheap as water."

The pipe operated for nearly 10 years, and records survive to show that there was more than one break in the line. But the biggest of them all, from what has been reconstructed so far, took place in the woods off Greenway Road, north of the base, in the property owned by a summer camp for Christian youth called Camp Good News.

The year was 1972. Dan Cullity, a Sandwich resident, remembers a town character by the name of Alvan Crocker talking about "a break in a fuel line that was running for days. The woods were soaked with it. Everything was soaked. I think he even said it had been hit with a bulldozer accidentally. . . They discovered this break because of the loss (of fuel) at the tank farm. Apparently it ran for days, but who knows?"

Written reports indicate that the break happened in 1972, and seem to corroborate local lore that a bulldozer hit the pipe. The documents also mentioned an amount:

"They called it a 2000-gallon spill," says Kreykenbohm. "But they really didn't know how much." Then why call it 2000 gallons? According to Albright, regulations at the time indicated that any spill greater than 50 barrels would require a full investigation and report. Spills of less than 50 barrels were considered to be minor. At 42 gallons per barrel, a 50-barrel spill meant 2100 gallons lost.

"So spills were automatically 2000 gallons," Albright concludes. "That way they didn't cross the threshold to report and do an investigation."

It would take 20 years before the true magnitude of what happened at Camp Good News would become apparent.

Meanwhile, a year after the spill, another unusually large slug of pollution made its way into disposal areas around the base. The reason was not that some remarkable new activity was underway, but rather that things were winding down, and the base was changing hands.

By 1973, the hospital was closing, soon to be demolished. BOMARC had shut down, rendered obsolete. The Connies no longer were flying. The Texas Towers had been dismantled. National Guard activity was steady, but certainly not frenetic. The Coast Guard, with its dramatic search and rescue mission in the waters of the Atlantic, had a full-time component, and a clear mission.

True, the Air Force was in the process of creating a new facility to carry out a traditional mission, beginning construction in a bullseye at the northern edge of the base on what has come to be called PAVE PAWS. This Precision Acquisition Vehicular Entry Phased Array Warning System, the only one of its kind on the East Coast, is a powerful microwave radar facility meant to make sure we can detect sneak attacks from nuclear missiles launched from submarines. As we will see, PAVE PAWS created its own environmental stir, and raised its own questions about health risks.

But PAVE PAWS did not pick up the tempo on the air base itself. In essence, the US Air Force was turning the keys over to the Massachusetts Air National Guard, who had a fixed wing jet fighter group training on and off the runways. Within the military bureaucracy, this meant that the Massachusetts Air National Guard would take control of the property. Which in turn meant that the Air Force, like any landlord about to transfer title, had to clean up the house first.

Retired Sgt. Mel Miller was one of the people working on base during the transition.

"When the Air Force left, there were all these paint lockers, chemical sheds, barrels of this and that," he remembers.

And what were the marching orders? "It was just, 'Get rid of it.' We'd load up a truck, and they'd take it out that night, and somewhere it went. Barrels of cleaning solvents, paint, normal flight line stuff. Where it went I don't know. But seeing as it was taken care of at night, it went to its own dumping site. I mean, why do it after dark? There was plenty of time during the day.

"Stuff that was labeled properly, and containerized well, that was disposed of properly. But material needs proper labels to be returned to supply. So that other stuff just disappeared. . . I'm willing to bet there's a lot of little dumps they haven't even discovered yet."

This was not 1943, or even 1953. This was 1973. Some people were beginning to realize that out of sight should not necessarily mean out of mind; there were regulations and procedures in place that were supposed to take environmental protection into account. But in the trenches, little had changed.

After control of the base was transferred, activity continued to scale down. Otis became one of only three Air National Guard bases nationwide; at 3000 acres, it is larger than some full-fledged, active-duty installations. As the new "landlord" of Otis, the Massachusetts Air National Guard became responsible for the physical plant—taking care of the runways, running the sewage treatment facility—as well as training civilian pilots to handle jet fighters. Since the late 1970s, the complement of jet fighters at the base has remained roughly steady, hovering around 15 to 18 aircraft.

"Basically, we did the intercept mission," says Air Commander Don Quenneville, who has served at the base since 1978. "We had a lot more 'Bear' (Soviet) activity then. . . Now, I think protection of the homeland is a very appropriate mission for the Air National Guard."

Many of the 40 pilots who come to Otis a handful of times a month to fly F-15 fighters are commercial pilots the rest of the week, changing uniforms and cockpits to keep their Guard status active. F-15s take off from Otis most mornings and afternoons—using techniques designed to minimize noise in local neighborhoods—for 90-minute missions over the Atlantic Ocean, practicing intercepts, aerial refueling, and "bumping heads," as mock dogfighting is called. At $35 million per aircraft, and millions more for fuel and maintenance, it is expensive practice.

Commander Quenneville is well aware that the activity of his group doesn't seem as vital or urgent as the military training of years past. But he believes the mission and the location remain essential. "As long as there is air sovereignty, we're in the right place for it," he says. The two long runways at Otis are a valuable asset, large enough to serve as an emergency backup landing site for NASA's space shuttles. Yet runway traffic is intermittent enough so that a major worry has become the chance of hitting deer which roam out of the woods and into the flight lines.

The Coast Guard, with an active duty component on the base, is clearly in the right place for the dramatic sea rescue work which hits the front pages of local papers periodically. Air Station Cape Cod is the largest such station on the East Coast, taking up 1400 acres and 352 buildings, home to 60 officers, 240 enlisted men and women, and 182 civilian personnel. The station mainly responds to search and rescue calls; by its own count over 7600 such missions have been flown over the past 23 years, saving nearly 2600 lives. Cape Cod teams have also responded to every major oil spill in the world in recent years, from the *Exxon Valdez* disaster in Alaska to the gigantic release during the Gulf War. The Coast Guard also is responsible for more than 600 housing units on the base, used by every branch of the service.

But in terms of land use, the huge bulk of the reservation is still used for Army Reserve and National Guard training. "Weekend warriors," as the National Guard are called, show up once a month for all types of training, reports Camp Edwards public affairs officer Jim Girard. Troops set up bivouacs in the woods, and maneuver as infantry units. Everyone qualifies on weapons, often machine guns or M-16 rifles. Navigation, communications, medical field work, are all covered. "35,000 troops trained here last year," says Girard.

Along Pine Hill, near the highest point of the reservation (which also happens to be the highest elevation above sea level on Cape Cod), stands the command post for the Impact Area, 2200 acres used for decades to test and fire all kinds of weapons. Of 23 ranges in the area, two are designed for demolition, testing plastic explosives and military TNT. The others are set up for various types of guns, everything from .45-caliber machine guns to mortars, and 60-ton cannon—all a far cry from the small weapons promised in the 1930s.

A company by the name of Avco, later to become Textron, also has used the area since the mid-1960s to test ballistics on a series of sophisticated anti-tank weapons. Small warheads, often bullet-shaped, are fired and studied to see how well they pierce thick armors. Although presently no "missiles" are fired in the area, reportedly various weapons have been fired both from the ground and from helicopters over the years. MX missile components also were tested years ago.

Captain Richard Nagle reports that tracer ammunition is most prone to causing brush fires, because a chemical coating on the round (which leaves the signature "tracer," a burning trail across the sky) might remain hot as it hits the ground. Bunkers and pits have been built to try to avoid ricochets and contain other forms of ammunition from smoldering in the pine woods.

The Impact Area has been used extensively for generations. Access to the area is restricted. "There's not a lot of it, but on any given ride you would come across some unexploded ordnance," Nagle adds. In years past, fires sweeping out of the Impact Area have burned woodland in Sandwich, in at least one case all the way to the edge of Route 6. The rumble and shake of bombs and artillery have also been companions to residents of the Upper Cape. Several years ago the base shifted to low-noise artillery shells, and replaced much of the live ammunition with dummy rounds to minimize noise and danger. How far noise from the blasts travels depends on weather conditions: on a clear day, large detonations don't echo off the clouds, but when it's overcast, "10 pounds (of explosives) will rattle windows," Nagle explains. From July 4 through Labor Day, artillery fire has been halted, "for the sake of our neighbors," he adds.

To avoid wildfires, areas of the Impact Area are "control burned" periodically. In general, the practice has worked, although a few years ago the "control" fire was set in the wrong location, beyond the breaks meant to hold it. Town firefighting companies from the Upper Cape had to be called in to battle the resulting blaze.

From the high vantage of Pine Hill and the Impact Area, Cape Cod looks virtually uninhabited, almost desolate. And back in the heart of the base, the sense is not too different. Of the dozens of barracks built in 1940, all have been razed except for six dilapidated specimens, waiting for funds to restore and preserve them as architectural relics. Open fields and empty, crumbling roads now feel fallow if not ghostly, nearly deserted if not abandoned. A railroad platform that once supported thousands of soldiers in transit now is a solitary cement slab, supporting weeds.

But if many of the structures have vanished, the memories have not. As public affairs officer, Jim Girard's responsibilities include escorting veterans who have returned to the base decades after their tour. Many of these men will stand in the open fields, he recalls, and say that this is where they slept, this is where they trained, this is where they became men, this is where some of the best friends of their lives were made. And some will leave tears for those friends who did not make it back home.

If that was the only legacy created by the military reservation, then our present relationship to this vast stretch of land (by Cape Cod terms) would be much simpler. But the past, unfortunately, has left behind some things more tangible than memories. And because of what was left, the Massachusetts Military Reservation has found itself forced once again—unwittingly, this time—into a position at the vanguard of a national movement:

Slowly, an environmental awareness was building in the country. Rachel Carson's "Silent Spring," Earth Day, gas shortages, Love Canal, Three Mile Island, hometown recycling committees, all contributed to a new consciousness, a new understanding.

And when environmental protection began to vie with military preparedness as a top priority, tension became inevitable. The conflict focused here. A challenge took shape, based at heart in a fundamental shift in thinking:

We need an entirely new way to locate, define, and battle "the enemy."

4

THE PLUMES

Denis LeBlanc is a mild-mannered scientist, rigorous and dogged, whose professional passion is groundwater. And so it wasn't clairvoyance or genius which led him to the first discovery of underground pollution seeping off the base. It was hard work mixed with a bit of luck.

When LeBlanc first started working for the United States Geological Survey, with offices at Woods Hole, various public officials around the state were beginning to grapple with what would become a crucial question: is the common practice of letting wastewater from sewage treatment plants leach into the ground a good idea?

"In 1977, early 1978, these officials asked us to pick a sewage treatment facility in Southeastern Massachusetts," LeBlanc recalls, "and do a case study: does it have an impact on groundwater or not? We selected the Otis Air Force Base plant for the study."

Why this plant, of the many in the region? "It was a federal facility, and it had been around for a long time," LeBlanc explains. "And most of the land around it was undeveloped, so drilling (test wells) wasn't so much of an issue. Those were the reasons why, not because any contamination had been discovered. I mean, the word 'plume' had been coined, but very few studies had been done at that time."

LeBlanc did what scientists still do, the only way they can investigate below the surface: he started digging wells, and testing the water that came up. "We looked for inorganics and detergents," he says, the sorts of things that sewage treatment plants might release. "Nitrates, chloride. We hadn't given volatiles [like gasoline or other chemicals that vaporize easily] so much as one thought."

It didn't take long for the results to come back, and the news was shocking. All these chemicals were sifting through the sandy soil, reaching groundwater below, and merging with that water as it flowed on its way toward the sea. "We had discovered a plume that was (two) miles long, and a half-mile wide," says LeBlanc.

The Ashumet Valley plume, as it came to be called, was moving south, between Ashumet Pond and Coonamessett Pond. It was well past the boundary of the base, creeping under homes and roads, merging with the groundwater as it made its way toward Vineyard Sound.

Here was proof that the rough maps of groundwater flow which Dr. Arthur Redfield had drawn in 1960, to warn against a nuclear park at Otis, were accurate. And this flow confirmed Denis LeBlanc's similar analysis, supported in sophisticated detail: the military base sits atop a virtual mountain of underground water which drains toward sea level, toward the bays and sounds around it, and toward the towns at its borders.

In this case, it so happened that hundreds of homes, most of them in Falmouth, were in the way. And most of the people who lived in those homes drank water pumped from private wells below.

It was a nightmare scenario, a creeping, invisible danger, like something out of a bad horror movie. And like the scientists in those movies, LeBlanc stuck with it, expanding the scope of his work. Before long, he would put in place a field of 1000 wells near the southern boundary of the base, to try to track movement of chemicals. And he went into the neighborhood of Ashumet Valley.

"We went out and sampled home wells," LeBlanc says, "and we couldn't determine anything. It was hit or miss." There were 300 or more private wells in the immediate area. It turned out, says LeBlanc, that only a handful of those were contaminated.

How could a well in the very path of the plume be clean? LeBlanc was developing a three-dimensional sense of what was happening: the plume was sinking deeper into the ground as it moved south.

"They (the private wells) were tapping the clean water above the plume, even though they were in it." One well at the Harney Golf Course, closer to the head of the plume, offered a dramatic example of the situation: the well was fairly deep, and contaminated. When the well was made shallower, the problems seemed to disappear.

But it wasn't as simple as that. For example, everyone could see that along the west side of Ashumet Pond, the side closest to the plume on what people call Fishermen's Cove, the rocks at the shoreline were pitch black. The rocks along the rest of the shore were white. What did that mean?

As it turned out, the change in color was not direct proof of the presence of oil or pollution. But for some reason, the metallic element manganese was coating the rocks. Manganese is released in what scientists call "anaerobic environments," meaning places where there is no air. And an underground plume could create exactly that kind of anaerobic situation. This was a tell-tale, a troubling signal. The plume became the key suspect.

And there was an even more ominous matter to consider. By sheer coincidence, just as Denis LeBlanc was beginning his studies, the town of Falmouth had built a brand new, million-dollar public water supply well in Ashumet Valley. It was a much bigger, deeper well than any private home would need, capable of delivering almost a quarter of all the water the town demanded, and by 1978 it was pumping away. The water had been tested at first, of course, and was fine. But if LeBlanc was right, and the plume was headed that way, and deeper wells were the ones likely to hit pollution, was this well delivering bad water to thousands of homes which had hooked up to the public water system?

LeBlanc tested the public supply well. "I just noticed it foamed," he says. "It foamed."

"We started getting foam in the area," remembers Ralph Marks, who worked in the Falmouth Water Department for 20 years before becoming superintendent of the Bourne Water District. "It got bad. People were calling and complaining. Where did it come from? . . . See, we never saw there was a sewage treatment plant up there. We never looked at what we now call the zone of contribution."

The public well was both deep and strong enough to draw the plume into its pipe, like a straw sucking juice from the bottom of a glass. There was only one thing to do.

"I shut that well down. I pulled the switch," remembers Ralph Marks. It was July, 1979. How long the water had been polluted was unclear. Later efforts to try to pump with less intensity, to avoid sucking the plume into the well, were not successful. For human consumption, the well is now useless.

"We lost 25 percent of our water supply, five million gallons, in one fell swoop," remembers Falmouth Selectman Virginia Valiela. For the past six years, Falmouth has been forced to impose water restrictions on its residents every summer.

Based in good part on LeBlanc's studies, Valiela and others in Falmouth were convinced that a plume from the base's treatment plant was the culprit. But within the military, there was no acknowledgement of that. "They gave no indication that they were responsible," says Valiela. "They were not looking beyond their borders."

Only in 1983, after nearly four years of meetings and dialogue, of pressure and politics, did the responsible officials on the base "step up to it," as Valiela puts it. Even so, it took until 1986 for Falmouth to receive funds to pay to bring public water into the areas which used to rely on private wells, and to reimburse town taxpayers for the cost of the polluted well.

Unfortunately, the Falmouth public well was not the first signal that there were underground problems at the base. In fact, it wasn't even the first well to be shut down. As far back as 1962, according to federal reports, a water supply well on the base known as the "B" well was found to be contaminated with the corrosive chemical "phenol" (also known as carbolic acid). Phenol is found in coal tar—it so happened that the coal storage area (which years earlier had been left unpaved to save expense) was near the well. The experience with B well didn't sound an alarm; it was no longer used for drinking water, but did provide irrigation for a military golf course.

A second well on the base, known as "G," was shut down much later, in 1985, because chemicals with tongue-twisting names like tetrachloroethylene and trichloroethylene were found in the water. Yet, according to Norm Therriault, Chief of Design and Engineering at the base through the 1970s and 1980s, people suspected that there were problems with groundwater (and possibly G well) as early as 1973 or 1974.

"In those days, environmentalists didn't have too much clout," smiles Therriault. Because his job description included acting as environmental officer, Therriault and base engineer Don Moncevicz organized regular meetings with their superiors to educate them to these concerns. These meetings began in the early 1970s.

"I was in charge of water pollution, so I'd give talks," Therriault recalls.

"We were explaining what happens to groundwater, how it gets contaminated, how it trickles into the ground and moves horizontally... We were hoping to make people aware that if they were dumping, it was going somewhere. We wanted to educate the brass, so to speak."

Moncevicz first arrived on the base in 1966 as a civil engineer. As the years passed, he says, "I started getting this better feeling for taking care of the land, but I wasn't the controlling mechanism. I and others could only recommend, but if we didn't have control, well. . ."

He remembers taking a walk one day during lunch, and coming across a burned area. It was one of the training sites for firefighting. People would store dozens of barrels of fuel in the area, not minding much if the barrels leaked, and then every month or so a billowing fire would be lit so the soldiers could learn how to handle the firefighting equipment.

"I went to my supervisor," Moncevicz recalls, "and I said, 'That doesn't look good to me.' I'm scratching my head. . . I mean, there's oil all over the ground. And I would report it. It was just common sense, my gut feeling. I'd hope they'd do something about it. But they generally wouldn't. No, they wouldn't."

Moncevicz also remembers visiting the BOMARC site in the years after the missiles had been dismantled, when it had become a maintenance area for heavy equipment like tanks and trucks.

"I told the Army I didn't like what I saw," he says. "There was oil all over the place. They didn't care. They had a million dollar machine that knocks down buildings, and I'm saying, 'Hey, you got to be careful with your oil.' And they just looked at me, and I looked at them."

As far along as 1983, a decade after Therriault and Moncevicz began their initial efforts, the US Army's Environmental Hygiene Agency reported serious deficiencies at Camp Edwards. The report's executive summary indicated that the base had not yet "fully implemented a hazardous waste management plan to include the spill prevention control and countermeasure plans." Past operations at the BOMARC site "may have contaminated the upper aquifer in this area." Batteries were not being disposed of properly. Hazardous wastes were being mixed with waste oil. And records were incomplete, "making it difficult to establish the identity, location, and rate of past generated hazardous wastes." Both Moncevicz's experience and this report from 1983 were danger signals, early warnings of a different nature than PAVE PAWS. Both implied that more problems would be found at the base than a single plume moving into Falmouth. Unfortunately, implication became proven fact; it took a growing national environmental awareness to trigger the necessary investigations.

By 1982, at the demand of Congress, the Department of Defense had created the Installation Restoration Program. The IRP, as it came to be called, had a clear mission: to identify, investigate, and hopefully clean up hazardous wastes from any areas under military control. The Massachusetts Military Reservation fit the bill.

One of the earliest reports, published late in 1986 after many months of work, was known as "Phase 1: Records Search. Final Report: Task 6." Although investigations of base pollution had been published even earlier, in 1983, this report was the first attempt to build a comprehensive overview of environmental problems. In a matter-of-fact tone, avoiding any semblance of sensationalism, it nevertheless presented graphic, disturbing information:

More than 60 possible pollution sites were documented, including three outside the present boundaries of the base. In the months ahead, the number of sites would continue to grow, until it approached 80. There were so many areas, with such different kinds of histories, that some kind of system had to be developed to differentiate them.

There were the "SD" sites, five of them, storm drainage ditches which caught any kind of runoff from runways, maintenance buildings, or the coal pile. Fuels, solvents, waste oils, coal dust and ash, all pooled in the ditches and then seeped toward the groundwater.

There were the "LF" sites, seven of them, landfills which at various points since the 1930s were used as dumps for everything from household waste to military ordnance, pesticides, paint, oils, car batteries, radioactive tubes, entire trucks— literal catch-alls for the base.

There were the "CS" sites, 18 of them, chemical spills of all descriptions, fuels and oils, solvents, antifreeze, paint, battery acid, lead, and unburned gunpowder.

There were the "FS" sites, 24 separate locations, fuel spills that all apparently took place since 1955. AVGAS, MOGAS, and JP-4 were fuels used for aircraft, hydrocarbons which in various forms also contained lead, and a potent carcinogen known as ethylenedibromide (EDB).

There were the "FTA" sites, three fire training areas which took hydraulics, transformer oil, solvents, heavy metals, and chemicals like polychlorinated biphenols (PCBs) to be burned.

There were the "CY" sites, four areas in the coal yards where phenols, sulfur, organics, and metals leached into the ground.

The situation was overwhelming, and murky. Of the 61 sites first identified, 46 were classified as having "potential for contamination." Of those 46, 37 were recommended for serious, detailed study.

It would take years, and tens of millions of dollars worth of work, to provide a clearer picture of the major plumes moving off the base. At some sites, little or no contamination was found, and the files on them were closed, while others only slowly gave up the secrets of what is happening below the surface.

As of 1994, these are the plumes which have been documented. Their size and locations are also shown on a map which accompanies this text:

1) The Ashumet Valley plume, caused by the base's sewage treatment plant, has grown to be over 18,000 feet long, 4000 feet wide, and has contaminated more than 13 billion gallons of groundwater. Not only are the wastes from sewage treatment in the ground, but also volatile organic compounds, solvents of the chloroethylene family. Seeping contamination from the primary Fire Training Area has merged with the treated effluent from the sewage plant.

2) The Landfill plume, known as LF-1, is a gigantic plume emanating from the dump, which was used on the base since the 1940s. Researchers working for the military found that there were different "cells" to the 100-acre landfill, reflecting different periods of activity, but all of them have merged into a plume which at latest report is 16,500 feet long, 6000 feet wide, and has contaminated 22 billion gallons of groundwater. The dump received fuel tank sludge, herbicides, solvents, batteries, DDT powder, hospital waste, sewage sludge, fire extinguisher fluid, and ammunition, in addition to household trash and chemicals. The plume has already passed under Route 28 as it moves west, approaching Route 28A and the village of Cataumet in Bourne. Two of the Bourne Water District's public supply wells in the area are directly in its path. These two wells account for 40 percent of the Town of Bourne's public drinking water.

3) The BOMARC plume, also known as CS-10, has reached 12,500 feet and spread 3600 feet wide, affecting 13 billion gallons of water. The contamination levels in this plume are extremely high, particularly for volatiles like

trichlorethylene (known as TCE): the federal government considers water dangerously contaminated when it contains more than five parts of TCE per billion parts of water; the water seeping out of the BOMARC site contains 3200 parts of TCE per billion parts water. Solvents used to clean the missiles, rocket fuel, carbolic acid, hydrazine, as well as waste from years of vehicle maintenance are all now in the aquifer. Although it is now clear that nuclear weapons were on the site, there has been no thorough investigation for radioactive contamination.

4) The West Truck Motor Pool plume, referred to as CS-4, seems to be a thin plume 11,000 feet long and 800 feet wide, which was caused by decades of dumping oil wastes and cleaning products in the ground around a service station for military vehicles. This plume begins within the BOMARC plume, and is moving under the Crane Wildlife Refuge which is next to the base toward Route 151 in Falmouth. This is the first plume which the cleanup personnel have tried to stop, using a line of wells which were dug south of the leading edge of the plume to pump and treat contaminated groundwater. The wells are meant to act like a fence, blocking the flow of pollution.

5) The Western Aquafarm plume was caused by leaks from an underground fuel storage facility, including old pipelines running out of the large tanks. For decades, huge amounts of fuel were stored in the area, conveniently located near the runways. Leaking fuel has created a carcinogenic soup of byproducts including benzene, ethylbenzene, toluene, and xylene, which is known as BTEX. The plume has spread 800 feet wide and 2000 feet long, moving south toward Ashumet Pond.

6) A storm drainage site, known as SD-5, is in the same area as the Western Aquafarm plume, and is responsible for another plume headed southeast into Johns Pond in Mashpee. Wastes from an inspection laboratory were poured into a "sump," a dry hole, which leached into the groundwater. These wastes include various chlorethylene chemicals found in cleaning solvents. The plume has moved 10,000 feet, and has spread 1750 feet wide.

7) The Petroleum Fuel Storage Area plume, PSFA, resulted from repeated spills of petroleum in the area where fuel was stored for all kinds of flight line operations. This plume is alongside the aquafarm plume, but it is distinct in part because it has extremely high levels of BTEX. 3250 feet long and 700 feet wide, 97 million gallons of water are now tainted. The plume is headed southeast toward Johns Pond.

8) The Eastern Briarwood plume seems to combine pollution from a

number of sources in what was an industrial area of the base. One site is Building 158, where maintenance of the "Connies" took place. Chlorinated solvents and fuel byproducts have now contaminated 160 million gallons. Although it appeared that this was a continuous, oval plume 2500 feet long and 1200 feet wide, it is now believed that there are a handful of "hot spots" in the area that are not connected.

9) The fuel dump test site, FS-1, is the area at the end of the runway where the release valves in the "Connies" were checked. Original estimates, based on the idea that the valves were checked before each flight, guessed that as much as six million gallons of fuel might have been left to seep into the ground at this site. However, first-hand reports say that the tests did not take place that frequently. Even so, hundreds of thousands of gallons of aviation gasoline might have been let loose in a designated dump site near the end of the runway. So far, some evidence of this spill has been found deep in the ground on the Mashpee side of the base, in the direction of Mashpee Pond. But a clear picture of what is there, whether it is a danger to the pond or the aquifer farther east, has not yet emerged.

10) The Sandwich pipeline spill, called FS-12, was caused in 1972 (according to local reports) by a bulldozer breaking the three-inch pipeline which ran from Cape Cod Canal to the base. As many as 70,000 gallons poured into the ground, creating a plume that is 5000 feet long and 2500 feet wide. One fuel additive which has shown up in this plume is ethylenedibromide (EDB), an extremely potent carcinogen. 1.5 billion gallons of water have been contaminated, and the plume is moving under Camp Good News toward Snake Pond, private homes, and a public water supply well in Sandwich.

The reason these plumes have become so big, and traveled so far, is that Cape Cod's sandy soil allows groundwater to migrate quickly. There is little clay, or hard till, which would slow the flow. That geologic fact, coupled with the geographic accident which places the base at the top of the aquifer, has put these plumes in motion as surely as rivers flow to the sea.

There is a rule of thumb which geologists use when they talk about how fast these plumes are moving: a foot a day. Maybe two feet a day in some places. That is every day, every plume. And because they spread as they move, as time passes they not only pollute more water, but become more difficult and more expensive to try to stop.

Ten major plumes have been identified in the decade since the IRP program began its work. It would be small comfort, but at least some comfort, to assume that by now we have located both the worst of what's out there, and all that needs to be found. Unfortunately, that is not necessarily the case, as a history of the discovery of the Sandwich pipeline (the cause of the most recently discovered plume) reveals.

None of the early investigations at the base put much emphasis on the Sandwich pipeline, for two reasons. First, the pipe and its maintenance had been the responsibility of a private contractor. And second, the records indicated a 2000-gallon spill; given the huge volumes of spills on the base itself, this seemed a relatively minor matter. No one investigated far enough to raise suspicion that the "2000 gallon" figure might be a convenient fiction used to avoid reporting the leak at the time. So FS-12, as it was known, was characterized as a low priority site.

It might have remained that way to this day, except that an elderly gentleman by the name of Wyeth Willard decided he wanted to make a contribution to the Town of Sandwich.

For 60 years, the Willards have run Camp Good News, a summer camp on 213 acres abutting the military base and Snake Pond. "My dad's a retired Presbyterian minister," explains Faith Willard, who now handles most of the camp's management. "And the sole purpose (of the summer camp) is to reach young people with the gospel of Jesus Christ." When her father first bought the land, Faith says, "he got down on his knees and prayed. He said, 'God, this is your land.' And we always felt that way." The camp has grown over the years; 250 boys and girls now come every summer.

As far as the Willards are concerned, the base has been "a wonderful neighbor. Every time those planes fly over, my dad would say, 'I thank God I live in America. I want to help the government all I can.'"

That desire led Reverend Willard to make an offer to the Sandwich Water District in the late 1980s. Water District Superintendent Bob Kreykenbohm remembers the proposal: "His idea was, 'Look, I own this camp. Do you want to acquire some of it for a well? The town's been good to me, I want to return something.' Of course, we jumped at it. That's free land, we're looking at." With the town growing so fast, it was getting hard to stay ahead of water demand, not to mention the trick of finding a clear 15-acre bullseye in which to plant a well and keep it protected from septic tanks.

In early 1990, the first pair of test wells went into the woods on camp property. "The engineer came back," remembers Kreykenbohm, "and he said, 'We've got a problem. It's foaming, it stinks, there's something wrong.' I thought it must be the contractor. So we checked the pipes—nothing. We got them steam cleaned—nothing in the process. So we moved 1000 feet back in the woods, and tried again."

The second set of wells came up even worse than the first. Kreykenbohm was looking at test results which showed something like 3000 parts of benzene for every billion parts of water—if benzene is present in more than five parts per billion, water is unsafe to drink. There was so much fuel coming up in those wells that it was possible, at one point, to take a match and light it. Bob Kreykenbohm has a little bottle on a shelf in his office filled with liquid pulled from the ground; pure JP-4 jet fuel, he says.

The only consolation was that the wells had hit what turned out to be dead center on the plume. Had they been a few hundred feet ahead of it, another million dollars might have been lost digging a well which would soon have been contaminated.

And so the question became, where is this stuff coming from?

"I knew there was a pipeline between the canal and the base," says Kreykenbohm. "But we didn't pay much attention. Hey, we were Sandwich, north of the base. All the pollution was south, in Falmouth and Bourne. But as soon as we found this—and we figured the groundwater was moving a foot or two a day— well, we went back 30 years and realized we were under the pipeline. All that was done in a matter of days."

Analysis of the plume showed a lot of benzene, but it showed something else as well. Ethylenedibromide, known as EDB, was also present in heavy concentrations. EDB was used for years as an additive in jet fuel. It is such a potent chemical that any water with more than two-hundredths of a single part of EDB per billion parts of water is considered unsafe to drink.

In effect, two plumes in one had been identified. The total spill, based on what was in the ground, was revised from 2000 gallons to something like 70,000 gallons.

"They were very upset," recalls Faith Willard, speaking of the Sandwich Water District. "But when they told me, it rolled off my back. I'm a Christian. I thought, 'This is God's work, and He's going to have to take care of it. We'll do the best we can, but it's in His hands.'"

Meanwhile, a serious debate had begun about who was responsible for doing the best we can. The National Guard was resisting all efforts to hold it accountable. Kreykenbohm remembers that the former head of the IRP, Ron Watson, said he needed absolute proof that this was base-related pollution, and Sandwich's investigation was not sufficient. Sandwich activist Susan Walker remembers Watson saying that because EDB had also been used as a farm fumigant that perhaps there were farmers in the area who were the source. Meanwhile, base personnel were insisting that their research showed nothing that could account for such a huge spill. And finally, the area was outside the base's boundaries anyway. This, apparently, was a crucial argument against the military taking the problem as its own.

Dan Cullity from Sandwich, who had known about the base in part because his grandfather worked there for years, began to wonder about that matter of boundaries. "It became a big question," he remembers. "In whose pasture was the ox gored?"

Cullity dug into his old family records and came up with geodetic survey maps made decades earlier. "The surveys showed that at other times, the base lines were quite different. . . And the (former) boundaries were pretty clear: all the area Kreykenbohm was coming up with was within the boundaries at that time." Faith Willard confirms this; she remembers the military using parts of the camp for maneuvers decades earlier. Why years of research by investigators under military contract never revealed this information remains unclear. Regardless, the map was a bombshell. By June, 1992, more than two years after the wells came up foaming, responsibility for the site was formally taken by the IRP. When the pipeline was dug up near the corner of Greenway Road, a section 40 feet long clearly was not original pipe, a sure sign there had been a repair if not a leak. Over the course of the next year, monitoring similar to what Denis LeBlanc had done in Ashumet Valley located the huge plume.

Faith Willard is not concerned that this plume is under the camp. The wells which provide her drinking water are shallow, and haven't been contaminated, she says. Even so, the military is going to pay to bring town water onto the site. "I think they're taking responsibility and doing all they can," she concludes. "This wasn't malicious. None of this was done on purpose."

Bob Kreykenbohm has more worries than that. Independent contractors he has hired have reported that one public supply well south of the spill will suck the plume into its pumps within 12 to 16 years, depending on how much water is pumped every day. Snake Pond, which is used for swimming by the public as well as Camp Good News, lies between the well and the spill, as do dozens of homes which have been converted to public water in the past few years. The good news is that so far, it appears that the plume is so deep it may actually pass under Snake Pond.

"We're still apprehensive," says Kreykenbohm, not even so much about the plume he knows as the ones he doesn't know about. The northern part of the military reservation is mainly woods and old dirt roads. Its bullseye is the Impact Area, but there are thousands of open acres outside that target. "Contractors could have dumped 10,000 gallons here or there," he says. "And that's like finding a needle in a haystack." There have been no comprehensive studies of this northern area to find out if Kreykenbohm's fears are justified.

And the pipeline itself remains where it was laid 20 years ago. It has not been dug up, removed, and examined for signs of other accidents. Legal disputes about who owns the pipe and who is responsible for the work have handcuffed the base, according to Ernie Keating, who is in charge of the military reservation's office for Unified Environmental Planning.

"They should just dig that up, right away," says Don Moncevicz, base engineer at the reservation for most of the time the pipeline was in service. "They should just do it. Dig it up right through the Town of Sandwich. Dig the whole bloody thing up. . . I really don't like that one."

As it turns out, another related spill has been identified and named. FS-13, within the confines of the base, is located farther south along this same pipeline. The spill has not been investigated with the same rigor as the others; the hope is that the spill, located near the site of other investigations, would have been detected if it was large. But the sketchy information available thus far, which at face value should be reassuring, is far from that. The reason? Records describe the size of FS-13 by using a familiar phrase:

"Approximately 2000 gallons," leaked in 1972.

Meanwhile, questions remain even about the very first plume which Denis LeBlanc found in Ashumet Valley. And the latest answers coming forward suggest that there is even more danger than has been described to the general public. That danger can be summed up in a word: phosphorous.

Used in detergents and fertilizers, phosphorous (a close relative of the better-known compound "phosphate") is an often-studied pollutant. When it enters lakes and ponds, algae and other small plant life go into a kind of feeding frenzy, multiplying like crazy, "blooming" so much that bodies of water can become covered with green gook. Fish and other life forms can be choked off.

Many sewage treatment plants send a lot of phosphorous into the ground; the plant at the military base was no exception. Yet, because of the way the Installation Restoration Program works, cleanup money has been dedicated for solvents and fuel spills, but not for phosphorous. The maps produced show the solvent plumes, and the fuel plumes; they don't show the phosphorous plumes.

Working with a small amount of independent funding, a neighborhood group called the Ashumet Valley Property Owners hired their own scientific consultants to look at the effects of the plume seeping through their community. "The overview," says Chris Dunn from the association, "is that Ashumet Pond is threatened by phosphorous from the plume. There's enough in the plume so that if it enters the pond, it will basically turn the pond into a swamp."

For reasons that are not entirely clear, it seems that solvents move underground much faster than this detergent contamination. "Phosphorous is retarded," says Dunn. "The toe of the plume is way down in East Falmouth. But the phosphorous is moving slowly in the pond's direction."

From a bureaucratic point of view, a solvent plume and a phosphorous plume are very different things: there is money to clean up solvents; there is no money to clean up phosphorous. Environmentally, of course, there is a strong similarity; either could wreak havoc on the pond, and destroy drinking water.

So even with all the study, the maps, and research over the past decade, the phosphorous danger has barely been discussed or mapped, let alone been the focus of a plan for treatment.

And when is this part of the Ashumet Valley plume expected to seep into Ashumet Pond?

"The time frame is now, the mid-90s," says Dunn. "The time frame is imminent. The ecological threat is real."

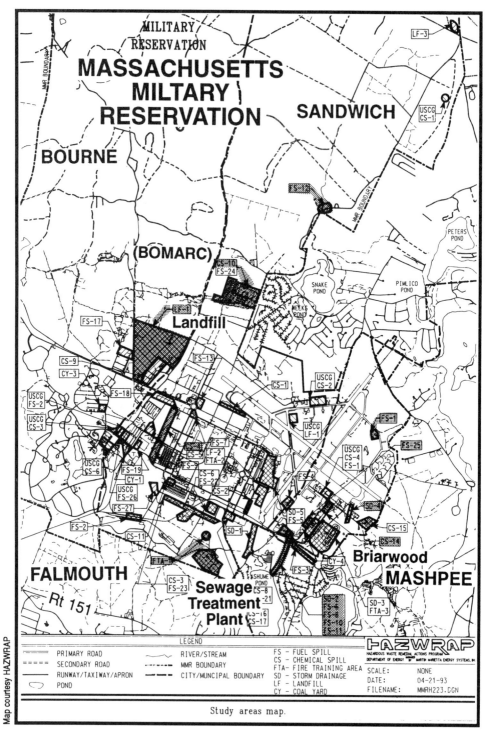

Map #3 Plume source areas.

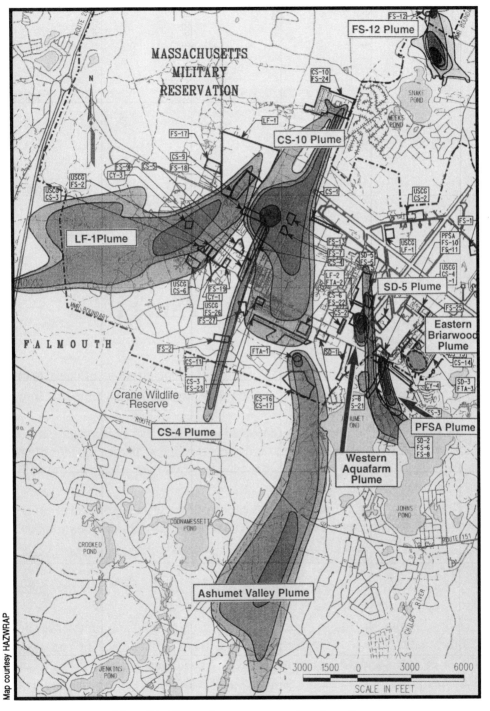

*Map #4 Groundwater contamination plumes
associated with source areas in map #3.*

5

DAMAGE, REAL AND PERCEIVED

The numbers associated with the damage, the repercussions of decades of a very different status quo, have swollen to such huge proportions that they become impossible to comprehend:

By June, 1994, best estimates reported that more than 53 billion gallons of the aquifer had been contaminated. And every day since, another eight million gallons more have been polluted as the plumes crawl their silent ways toward the sea.

Grasping the concept of 53 billion gallons of water is beyond any human mind. Even so, these kinds of raw numbers reverberate through communities. The waves of shock can create as much—or even more—damage as the plumes themselves.

Scientists like Denis LeBlanc will try to offer people some facts that, even if they are not reassuring, at least are meant to keep panic at bay:

Keep in mind that these plumes are very deep by the time they leave the military base. Know that contamination in them is measured in parts per billion of water and so sometimes it is not considered harmful. Remember that most private wells sit dozens of feet above the pollution; the maps which show the spread of these plumes need to be understood in three-dimensional terms. Yes, these plumes seem to be seeping into Johns Pond, and Ashumet Pond, yet the pollution seems to be disintegrating when it reaches air and has

52

been difficult to find so far. There are even some bacteria, living bugs, that thrive on petroleum, and seem to be neutralizing some of the problem some of the time.

Yet this information is small comfort to those who live above this contamination, or those who can look at the map and see quite clearly that they are in its path. And so the damage meted out must be seen not only in environmental terms, but also in the psychological harm inflicted home by home, in the loss of everything from peace of mind to confidence in the military as a good neighbor. All this translates into a tangible hurt as well, as property values decline around the site.

George Schuck, whose family has been running the S & P Service station on Route 28A in Cataumet since 1961, found himself face to face with many of these questions. Schuck grew up in Bourne. Now 50 years old, he remembers going to the very landfill which is now seeping in his direction "to shoot rats in the dump as a kid," a popular local pastime. He remembers watching the "Connies" take off, and the way military personnel filled the town. He served in the Air Force in Selma, Alabama, and when it came to disposing of waste, "we did the same things there." He took over the family business in 1983, delivering home heating fuel and pumping gas from an old-fashioned service station.

The station looks funky, but the fuel storage is state of the art. Schuck spent more than $200,000 in 1991 to comply with every federal and state requirement, to make sure he wouldn't be putting any pollution into the ground. He was one of the first fuel dealers in the area to do it, and he admits he had to be pushed. "The government made me change those tanks," he explains, and now he's glad it's done.

So you might imagine George's surprise, and dismay, to find out in 1993 "that this plume is heading towards us. I'm located practically in the center of it." And when Schuck began to listen to what base officials were saying about the situation, he was shocked yet again. "They said they were just going to let it go out to Buzzards Bay," he recalls.

This was indeed the initial position of base officials, that the plume was so deep that it could be left to trail into the ocean. But between the edge of the plume and Buzzards Bay stood dozens of businesses, hundreds of homes, two large public supply wells, and fertile shellfishing areas. To George Shuck, one of many people caught in the middle, the military's stance smacked very loudly of a double standard.

"To do all that work," George muses, talking about his own business, "and then have the government saying, 'We'll just let it go right under you,' well. . . Let me put it like this: I expect no less of the government than the government expects of me."

Schuck became involved with what came to be known as "the LF-1 Committee," a group from Bourne led by one of Schuck's neighbors, George Seaver.

"I work right here (in Cataumet), and I live on Mystery Lane," says Seaver. "I looked out the window one day and saw a truck digging a hole in the ground. It was February, I think, 1993. I asked what they were doing. They said they were drilling to monitor for contaminants. Now, I'd known vaguely about the plume, but I had no idea it was so close."

It was a profoundly unsettling moment, although Seaver would later find out that the well being dug was checking the height of the water table in the area, not searching for a plume that had not yet arrived. Before long, Seaver was pulling the committee together, and using his engineering background to help dig into the issue himself. The more he studied, the more certain he became that the military's position—that the plume would pass harmlessly out to sea—was wrong.

A big part of the reason the plume falls deeply into the ground, Seaver realized, is that rain water falls on top of it, and gravity draws the water down. But as the groundwater reaches the coast, it begins to rise again. "It runs into the oceanic water table," Seaver explains. "Light, fresh water can't go under the heavy salt water, generally. So the water table rises above the ocean. The (fresh) water returns at or about the coast." This means that the pollution would re-emerge somewhere along or near the shoreline.

In addition, closer to the sea there is less buffer offered by the land itself. "Land at Otis is as much as 300 feet above sea level," Seaver reasons. "Down here we're getting closer to the water table—and the water table is getting closer to us."

He wasn't certain what this all might mean for hundreds of private wells in the path of the plume. He didn't know for certain if the fresh water he could see streaming into the bay along the shoreline might be this deep water coming to the surface in shellfish beds. But even if all his suspicions turned out to be groundless, he became convinced this plume should be contained.

"We see the greatest threat to be economic," Seaver concludes. The immediate effect, he says, is that banks have become leery about loaning money to businesses located above a plume of hazardous waste. "Mortgageability is shot," says Seaver, citing anecdotes from neighbors. And national studies produced by the LF-1 Committee showed that property values in other areas similarly affected by pollution drop by as much as 15 percent.

Based on this kind of work, the group approached Bourne Town Meeting in the spring of 1994 with a resolution calling for "immediate plume containment." A map with a spreading red stain showed the path of contamination, accompanied with a headline: "If you are on this map—then your property values are affected. . . Stop the plume. . . if not, the red stain is forever." The resolution passed by an enthusiastic, unanimous voice vote.

There is evidence much closer to home that pollution creates a climate of concern, which in turn has hit property values. James Kinney from Mashpee, who has investigated the issue and been a strong advocate for a cleanup of all the plumes, gathered information which showed serious impacts. For example, a home on Cranberry Avenue near Johns Pond in Mashpee, in the area of one of the plumes on the eastern side of the base, sold for $173,500 in 1988, and resold for only $102,000 in 1992. Another home on the southern side of Johns Pond sold for $172,500 in 1988, and resold for $126,000 in 1993.

It is difficult to put a hard figure on how much of these kinds of losses are due to the plumes, and how much is due to a general decline in property values across Cape Cod during a recession. But there is no doubt the problem is real, and the plumes are a factor.

For State Representative Eric Turkington from Falmouth, whose district has been hit by several plumes, there is "no question. The whole Ashumet area, and Perry Road is affected. . . Stuff just doesn't move. I know someone in the real estate business who has his own home for sale, on one of the ponds. It's been three years, and there are no offers."

As the first town to document pollution in drinking water, Falmouth also was the first town to get compensation for the damage. It took nearly seven years from the time Falmouth's public well was closed, but in 1986 the military reimbursed the town nearly $4 million to help pay for work needed to install town water, and dig a new well. Some feel that the town could have cut a better deal, and gotten more money—although at the time this was a breakthrough agreement. The money and the work did much to ease concern among the people already in the neighborhood, but it didn't erase what had become a stain in the public's mind.

"You can talk 'til you're blue in the face," Turkington says. "You can tell people about town water, that the plume is deep. But they all have the idea of their kids swimming in the pond, and coming out with lesions."

"We have numerous homes around Johns Pond that aren't selling," confirms Mashpee Selectman Nancy Caffyn. "It is clearly that people are selling in a panic, and at a loss. At the Otis Trailer Park, people won't even park their trailers."

"What the real estate agents say to me," reports Falmouth Selectman Virginia Valiela, "is that a house stays on the market longer, and the price gets reduced before it sells."

"The feeling among many people," adds Bourne Selectman Haydon Coggeshall, "is that they want out."

Juan Bacigalupi didn't want out. Juan enlisted in the Army, then joined a military intelligence unit in 1975. He participated in Desert Storm. Emergency medicine is his field, and he moved his family to Cape Cod early in 1993 to begin work at the Cape & Islands Emergency Medical Services System. The house he decided to buy was located right between Ashumet Pond and Johns Pond in the Briarwood section of Mashpee, on a handsome acre of land. "They were asking $169,000," he remembers. "We got it for $129,900."

He assumes that much (maybe even all) of that $40,000 difference was because of the plumes. Juan was aware of the situation when he bought the house; right at the corner of his property sits a monitoring well, installed by crews from the base. It has come up clean—the first to do so in a line of wells running through the neighborhood. The Bacigalupi family drinks out of their own private well. Everyone in Briarwood on the other side of the monitoring well has been put on town water.

"My well is 20 feet or so deep," Juan says. "The contamination is at 140 feet. . . . Do we feel safe? Yeah. If we didn't we'd be on town water right now."

Juan finds that many of his neighbors seem to avoid talking about the problem which has crept into their lives. "It's not really spoken about by a majority of the people here," he muses. Maybe there is some denial at work, maybe people are afraid that the more they talk, the more their property values will drop. "Maybe it's the typical thing, 'I don't want to get involved,'" Juan concludes.

One person who got involved early, and stayed involved, is Al Orlando. Orlando was president of the Briarwood/Mashpee Association. He represented his neighborhood in negotiations with the base for five years, until an agreement signed in 1991 spelled out exactly what the base would do to help people living above the Briarwood plume.

"The military kept telling us the contamination was too deep to affect our wells," Orlando remembers. "Yet we had two wells 90 feet deep that showed contamination. They refused to accept that."

The base might not have accepted it, but the State of Massachusetts felt there was a clear risk. For five years, bottled water was supplied to hundreds of people in the Briarwood area. "The state picked up the tab," says Orlando.

Meanwhile, "the Mashpee Board of Health imposed a moratorium on building. No one could build a house. And you couldn't do anything with property. Basically, you couldn't sell it."

The agreement finally hammered out gave $1000 to homeowners in East Briarwood to pay for hooking into town water. It gave $500 to homeowners in West Briarwood (where base officials claimed pollution was not as pervasive) for the same service. The base also paid a large percentage (but not all) of the cost of designing and building a new public water system for Mashpee, including more than $1 million for a well site. All this was meant to compensate for damage done, even though the base insisted that the plumes were not harming the shallow private wells.

The specter of the problem continues to reach into the surrounding neighborhoods. Orlando knows of a case in which a homeowner went to a local bank for an equity loan. The home is located on Johns Pond, but was not in any physical way affected by the plume moving off-base. "The bank wouldn't give them the loan because they didn't have town water," he says. "There was nothing wrong with them, nothing wrong with their well, but that didn't matter."

"A lot of it is fear, really," says Tom Cambareri, who works for the Cape Cod Commission on groundwater problems around the peninsula. "Fear of the unknown. People from Truro will call my office and say, 'We have a sole source aquifer here on Cape Cod. Is the Massachusetts Military Reservation contaminating our water?'" Cambareri explains that Truro's groundwater, 60 miles away from the base, is not affected.

Reading the maps, analyzing the available information, has taught Juan Bacigalupi a lot about the neighborhood he has adopted. He sees that the surface of Ashumet Pond is several feet higher than Johns Pond, so he knows which direction the water is draining. He worries more about the groundwa-

57

ter than the ponds themselves, because he believes these chemicals will "volatize" when they hit the air ("That's why they call them 'volatiles,'" he smiles). Yet all that said, the Bacigalupis' two children are allowed to swim there only occasionally. "My wife doesn't want the kids to take swimming lessons in the ponds," says Juan.

No one could accuse Juan Bacigalupi of being anti-military, but he has strong words of criticism for his neighbor. He has become deeply skeptical of how the situation is being handled. Years of denial, followed by what in his opinion have been years of procrastination, have left him troubled and angry. He takes those feelings right up the military chain of command, to the general in charge of the base:

"He has sworn an oath to the United States Constitution," says Bacigalupi. "He is supposed to protect and defend the citizens. It never says just to protect against the Bad Guys overseas. It says protect and defend, period. I think the Commanding Officer is violating that oath. . . Otis needs to be cleaned up because it's causing a disaster for these communities."

The Bacigalupis have had some experience with community disasters: years ago, Juan's wife Karen lived near the Three Mile Island nuclear power plant. She has successfully overcome health problems which she suspects were caused by radioactivity released during the plant's famous accident.

And on Cape Cod, there is reason to fear that pollution from the military base may have done damage of a similar kind, damage not just to property values, or peace of mind, or to people's trust in the military, but damage to public health as well.

6

CANCER, THE BIG SCARE

Terry White is fooling around with the engine of Wellfleet's harbor patrol boat, hanging around the dock, nodding and talking with so many people who pass by that you'd swear he was a Wellfleetian born and raised.

But in fact, Terry White was born in West Falmouth. Strong and hefty, Terry lives what looks like a typically active life for a healthy, physical 37-year-old on Cape Cod. He loves to scuba dive and does it every chance he gets. He also juggles three jobs: as a medical technician for Outer Cape Health Services, he takes care of lab work, EKGs, whatever support the doctors and nurses need. His own business is animal removal, going after raccoons and squirrels that invade houses, promising that he'll relocate the offending beasts without killing them. And he serves as an EMT, firefighter, and head of the dive rescue squad for Wellfleet.

But in fact, Terry White is anything but typical. Actually, he is something of a walking miracle, because back in March, 1993, his doctor told him he had one month to live. Lymphoma was killing him.

The miraculous part is that Terry's cancer is in remission—for the moment. "I live three months at a time now," he says. "I get tested every three months." He is not sure why the tumor which was pushing against his aorta has shrunk, but he thinks it has to do with alternative therapies he started after the chemotherapy didn't work too well. He wonders if it has anything to do with his state of mind, trying to avoid stress; maybe it has to do with the water pressure from all the deep diving he refused to give up. He is not into hocus pocus, he works in a modern medical facility, but he has come to believe that attitude plays a part in fighting cancer.

"I went straight to acceptance," he says, "because I know where this came from."

It came, he believes, from the Massachusetts Military Reservation.

White's relationship with the base began as a child, because his father was a Falmouth cop ("a 30-year man," says Terry) who worked security at the base, hung out, socialized for decades out there. "I grew up playing with those kids, I grew up around all those ponds," he says. Even after his parents separated and his mother moved to Eastham, Terry spent every summer around the base. He would dive, catch fish. When he was old enough he and his buddies used to drive around the dirt roads of the Impact Area "for kicks."

When Terry joined the Coast Guard, it was only natural that he would be stationed at the base. The year was 1976. He was working with boilers and other machinery, taking waste oil or hydraulic fluid and dumping it out back so it wouldn't dirty up the hangar—no one giving too much thought to whether that was the greatest thing in the world to do.

"Most of the guys I was stationed with were 20 years old," he recalls. "The biggest priority was going to the bar that night, seeing what might happen. People didn't care. You did your duty, and that was it."

He remembers it wasn't too unusual to find old ordnance laying around in the woods. But what was really striking was when he dove in the three ponds nearby where his father had taken him as a kid; Johns, Ashumet, and Snake:

"All through those ponds, there was live ordnance (on the bottom). I found mortars in there, and 50-caliber (rounds)." To this day, Terry will sit down with a map and mark the locations: the southeast corner of Snake, the most northern hook of Johns, the northeast and northwest corners of Ashumet. "And those ponds were where I spent most of my time."

When health problems first reached into Terry White's life, they came by way of his father.

"Nobody in my family ever had cancer," he says. "Neither side." But in the mid-1980s, doctors found a tumor in his father's kidney. "They removed his kidney. But then a couple of years later he had a brain tumor. They operated and cut it out as well. Then a second brain tumor took him." Terry's father died in 1988.

It wasn't until the summer of 1992 that Terry began experiencing his own problems. He woke up with chest pain, shortness of breath, as if he'd had a heart attack. At first he was diagnosed as having a form of muscle inflammation. It took a month before a chest x-ray showed a tumor in what is called the "aortic window." A biopsy showed large-cell type B lymphoma, a particularly virulent form.

"In my mind I know where it's from," says White. "It's the toxics I was exposed to." In particular, he believes, the dangerous chemicals that live ordnance release as they break down in water are the most likely pathway.

Life became a battle. Thirty-five cycles of radiation didn't eliminate the tumor. There was talk of a bone marrow transplant, then a decision that it was too late, there was nothing to be done. Weak as he was, Terry kept diving because he felt better in deep water. He tried to reduce stress, he drank an herbal remedy inspired by Native American medicine. When he returned for what people assumed would be one of his last checkups, the miraculous had happened: the tumor was undetectable.

The remission is remarkable, but White isn't pronouncing himself cured. "I'll be lucky if I have five years," he figures.

Terry White knows he can't prove it; he knows some people will dismiss his family's story as coincidence, but he is absolutely sure that the link between his father's death and his illness, between the unusual cancers now in the family history, has everything to do with the environment around the military base:

"I'd love to see the government contact people who lived on the base, who served on the base even for three or four weeks, and study their health histories," he muses. "But the government will never do that. It would be opening themselves up to too many lawsuits."

And so, says White, "I'm not even a statistic, when it comes to the cancer stuff. I'm not even in those studies."

The "studies" Terry is alluding to comprise some of the most disturbing and controversial information to emerge from what would seem, on the surface, to be the most logical, simple, and important questions:

What damage has pollution from the base done to public health? Have these chemicals, with their potential for causing cancer, truly brought the disease into the lives of Cape residents?

As it turns out, trying to answer these questions led to unexpected, shocking revelations: cancer rates across Cape Cod are elevated, among the highest in all of Massachusetts, and no one can say exactly why. People hurry to dismiss this finding by saying that the Cape's population has an unusually high number of retired people, and older people are more prone to cancer. Yet these figures have been carefully adjusted to take age into account; young or old, Cape Codders have more cancer than people their own ages who live elsewhere. Meanwhile, that fact does not begin to satisfy people trying to comprehend and measure what role the military base might have played in the high number of cancers in the Upper Cape area alone, in the neighboring towns of Sandwich, Falmouth, Bourne, Mashpee, and Barnstable.

Like many things about the military reservation, the exploration of a possible link between decades of various activity and present-day illness has become a symbol, a case study for efforts to try to make this important connection anywhere in the country. And the person who made the connection, who demanded answers the loudest and the earliest, was Dr. Joel Feigenbaum from Sandwich.

Joel Feigenbaum has been described by various people at various times as brilliant, cantankerous, manipulative, blunt, confrontative, alienating, public-spirited, and self-serving; as a true democratic voice and an inflexible monomaniac; as the most important force for military cleanup and as the biggest obstacle to a constructive meeting of the minds. He has been a catalyst, a lightning rod, and a bulldog about the base. He has staked out radical positions; in effect he has made room for more moderate voices to negotiate and communicate "within the system," in the space to his right. He is willing to call the head of the local cleanup office "a good Nazi," and accuse elected officials and other community activists of allowing themselves to be "co-opted and used" because they don't agree with all his tactics. He has been arrested, excluded from meetings, attacked in print by military personnel, but he has outlasted many of his critics and now sits on the panels which have helped make key decisions about the Upper Cape's environmental future.

This is the Joel Feigenbaum most local people have read about in the newspapers, whose name has become synonymous with opposition to much of what the military wants to do on Cape Cod.

The Joel Feigenbaum most people don't see is a theoretical physicist who got his PhD from Cornell in 1970, who is a tenured professor of mathematics at Cape Cod Community College, who is at home with equations, probabilities, and statistics.

So Joel Feigenbaum the activist raised the cancer questions, but Dr.

Feigenbaum the mathematician began coming up with some of the answers.

"Most of my time has been spent on the cancer issue," he says. "Not just as an activist, but as a scientist and mathematician. . . And in 20 years, that's what people will remember: that I discovered the cancer issue."

It didn't take long for Joel to begin to wonder whether the pollution from the base could be shown to cause cancer in the surrounding towns. The year was 1985. Fragmentary reports had surfaced months earlier, indicating there might be unusual amounts of certain cancers on the Cape, but the data was sketchy.

It so happened that Joel knew the state employee who ran the "cancer registry" for the Massachusetts Department of Public Health from his days organizing in Lynn, so he gave a call:

"I asked, 'Hey, what's the story?' And he said to me, 'There's all this mortality data going back to 1969.'"

Needless to say, Feigenbaum asked for copies of all the information. For months, nothing arrived. In August, 1985, after some pushing and prodding, the numbers finally showed up. "That's when all hell broke loose," Joel remembers.

Working through a thicket of figures, Feigenbaum began reporting detailed results culled from the raw data—a process he continued year after year into the 1990s. He compared reported cancers from the Upper Cape with reported cancers across the state, and in the communities of the Lower Cape. These figures were adjusted for age, because Cape Cod has an older population than many parts of the state. He recognized that many people have moved to the Cape in recent years, but he theorized it wouldn't make sense for those people to be bringing more cancer with them than anyone else of their same ages. He tried to reduce the variables, and hone the data in different ways.

"I had to learn how to use a spreadsheet on the computer, to put this together," he recalls.

Over and over again, the figures came back showing that there is something drastically wrong in these communities:

From 1969 through 1983, women living in the five Upper Cape towns reported 1486 cancers of all kinds. The state average for women of the same age was 1335 cases. While the numbers may not sound dramatic, they translate into a cancer rate more than 11 percent above average.

From 1982 through 1985, men on the Upper Cape reported 251 prostate cancers, 39 percent more prostate cancers than the state average.

Women from Bourne and Falmouth, in particular, had dramatically higher cancer rates than women from most towns in the state. People from Bourne tend to live nearer the base, and live near the base more years. But breast cancer among women in all five Upper Cape towns was almost 25 percent higher than average in the early 1980s.

From 1982 through 1984, men on the Upper Cape had been diagnosed as having cancer of any kind at a rate 13 percent higher than the state average. Women had been diagnosed at a rate 19 percent above average. Because women for many years tended to be at home more than men, the difference in rates suggested that if the environment played a role in creating these cancers, the cause might be located in or around the home.

Regardless, one thing was clear: the raw numbers were large enough, and the rising rates dramatic enough, to be able to say that the possibility this was some fluke, some accident or coincidence, was virtually nil.

When the data showed up in the local media, a storm of concern broke over Cape Cod. In the fall of 1985, local hearings with representatives from the Massachusetts Department of Public Health were held to discuss the high numbers. Paul Brodeur, a nationally-acclaimed investigative journalist who was delving into the import of these high cancer rates, remembers that state officials came to the Cape and told people that they were smoking and drinking too much, eating too much greasy food, "and that was the reason for these cancer elevations."

But Joel had his own theories. They all revolved around the military base, and they all needed additional study. He wanted to see if there was a connection: look at people who have lived near the base for a long time. Look at people exposed to drinking water that might have been contaminated by previous base activity. Look at people who live near the fire training areas, where smoke might carry over their homes. Look at people who live near the Impact Area, where gunpowder was burned.

Meanwhile, other people had other theories about what was beginning to look like a public health crisis uncovered. Paul Brodeur, for instance, suspected that the Air Force's huge microwave radar station, PAVE PAWS, was bombarding the Upper Cape with radiation which could trigger cancers; as far back as 1978, when PAVE PAWS was first turned on, he had predicted that elevated cancer rates would be detected.

Yet PAVE PAWS could not explain high numbers of cancer as far back as 1969, nearly 10 years before it was turned on.

And then, as data from the rest of Cape Cod came to the surface, it became clear that this was a problem of the entire peninsula, not just the towns around the base. Breast cancer among women in the 10 towns of the Lower Cape was more than 14 percent higher than state averages; prostate cancer among men was more than 33 percent higher. Exposure to the Massachusetts Military Reservation couldn't explain that. Could the Cape's reliance on drinking water from its own sandy soil have something to do with it? Could the high-tension power lines which run down the spine of the Cape, close to many homes, be emitting harmful electro-magnetic energy? And why were figures for tiny Truro so high? Could that have something to do with activity at the North Truro Air Force Base; perhaps radar, or other kinds of dumping; could the sample be too small to tell an accurate story?

The questions were valid, but as far as Joel Feigenbaum was concerned, they were drawing attention away from his main concern: the Upper Cape cancer rates were, across the board, even higher than the Lower Cape's. "Standardized Incidence Ratios," comparing all cancers on the Upper Cape with all cancers on the Lower Cape from 1982 through 1985, showed more than 15 percent more cancers in the towns around the military base. Colorectal cancer, and lung cancer among women, were especially high. Dr. Feigenbaum argued that serious, well-funded studies should begin immediately to find out why.

More than talk about the pollution of the past, more than concern about how the base was participating in the military conflicts in Central America in the 1980s, the cancer issue brought people out of their homes in support of Feigenbaum's crusade. May 17, 1986, 300 people protested at the main gate to Otis; one of their demands was for the kind of public health studies needed to answer Joel's questions. Before the day was done, 32 were arrested, charged with disorderly conduct. As might be expected, Joel was among them.

Of all those arrested, only Joel Feigenbaum ever went to trial. "In our opinion, Feigenbaum was the leader of the demonstrators," Cape and Islands District Attorney Phillip Rollins announced, adding that the others would not be prosecuted.

The courtroom and trial became a stage for a broad discussion of military attitudes, as well as the "coverup," to use Joel's term, by the state Department of Public Health.

Feigenbaum argued that his protests were necessary because there was a form of conspiracy which was both contributing to cancer on Cape Cod, and sending American boys to undeclared conflict in Central America. The base was serving as a symbol of militarism in general, and as a hazardous waste danger in particular.

This was exactly the kind of publicity Feigenbaum was looking for. And he was able to deliver some compelling support for his conspiracy theory:

"The powers that be in the department didn't want to find out what was going on," testified Joel Swartz, who was the director of risk assessment for the state Department of Public Health. "They wanted to keep people in the dark and keep them guessing. They were afraid we would have found something." Swartz said he resigned his position because political interference made it impossible for him to do the studies he thought necessary.

Such testimony was meant to support a "necessity" defense, that this demonstration blocking the roadway was necessary because there was an imminent danger to the public. But the jury was not convinced. Feigenbaum was found guilty. Then the judge announced the sentence: two months in prison. The judge ignored the District Attorney's suggestion that the case be put "on file" with no jail term.

Newspaper editorials rushed to the "citizen activist's" defense: "The streets will not be any safer during the two months that Joel Feigenbaum spends in the county jail—if he loses on appeal," wrote *The Falmouth Enterprise.*

It took two years and thousands of dollars in legal fees before Feigenbaum won his appeal. He never went to jail, and in the meantime he had won two more victories: first, virtually everyone now knew about him and about the problems at Otis. And second, the Department of Public Health agreed to fund an independent study of cancer on the Upper Cape.

There was wrangling about the amount of money to be committed, and what should be studied, but by 1988 a team of researchers from Boston University received a promise for $500,000 to do their cancer study for the Upper Cape. Led by Ann Aschengrau, then assistant professor of public health at BU, with co-investigator Dr. David Ozonoff, BU professor of environmental health, the team began what they hoped would be one of the most exhaustive and comprehensive looks at the population of the Upper Cape towns which ring the military base.

The goal "was to try to find out if the cancers in the Upper Cape were related to environmental exposures," remembers Ann Aschengrau. "That meant the base, but not exclusively related to the military base."

Thousands of households were called, hundreds of people interviewed. There were "dead controls," meaning information about several thousand of the deceased was analyzed. Work history, health history, and geography were covered. The questions ran an extraordinary gamut:

Did you ever serve at Otis? Did you ever work in a cranberry bog? Do you live near an airport runway? Do you smoke cigarettes? Did you ever smoke a pipe? Are you on public water or private water? Do you drink bottled water? How about beer or wine? Ever hold a full-time job? Were you born in the United States? Did you ever dye your hair? Did you ever eat seafood from Boston Harbor? Were you ever a ham radio operator? Did you swim in Johns Pond? What is your religion? How old were you when you first started menstruating? Do you eat the tamale from lobsters? Do you take mostly showers or baths?

The survey was remarkably broad: "scattershot," Feigenbaum would later charge. It took until September, 1991, for the results to be published. A gigantic volume of information and analysis was released. "It was a $500,000 study," asserts Aschengrau, "but we gave the state a million dollars worth of work for that $500,000."

Despite all this effort, despite all this money, the BU study didn't answer the crucial questions: why is there more cancer on the Upper Cape, and is the military base the reason?

"After an extensive review of the environmental factors it is clear that there was ample cause for concern," the report announced. That much was well known; that was why the study had been funded. And yet the authors could not explain "more than a small part of the cancer increase in the region." The best hope, the study concluded, is that their work could "succeed in shrinking the large area of uncertainty regarding the influence of various environmental factors and provide a basis to ask further questions. We leave it to the Reader to judge how well this has been accomplished."

That kind of conclusion fell far short of what the general public had been hoping to hear. Yet there were specific results that pointed to a few key concerns:

The study reported that in areas around the Impact Area, close to specific gun and mortar positions, there was an increase in lung and breast cancer—although the numbers the study was working with were so small that it was difficult to guarantee there was any clear cause and effect.

The report also noted that people who swam in Johns Pond seemed to have a higher chance of contracting brain cancer, although the chances didn't seem to increase the more you swam in the pond. One puzzling finding suggested that the brain cancers actually decreased the more people swam in the pond, although further analysis discounted that interpretation. Yet again, the raw numbers were so small that proof-positive was elusive.

Meanwhile, there were hints of problems in other areas. People who lived near cranberry bogs for a long time seemed to have more cancer; there was also concern expressed for people supplied by water districts whose pipes contain traces of the chemical PCE. And there was the suggestion that women who live near the military base for more than 20 years contract cancer more often than women who do not live near the base.

For Joel Feigenbaum, the study he had forced into existence was deeply unsatisfying. He pointed out flaw after flaw: it didn't include cancer data after 1987. It didn't break out men versus women until he pressured them to do so. A long delay in releasing the data was "wholly irresponsible." He found "extreme bias" in the analysis, which he said skewed the findings against identifying a relationship between cancer and base activities.

"First you fight to get the study," he says. "Then you fight for the methodology. Then, the way the data is reported— it's hidden, or they screw around with the data. . . It's not that these people are lying bastards. They're under tremendous pressure."

Ann Aschengrau sees her work in entirely different terms. "I think it's a really good first step in evaluating the connection between cancers and the pollution," she says. She advocates continued study of the area. Ponds should be tested more carefully. "The whole hot spot analysis should be done. We should be looking for cancer hot spots in the community," and not allowing ourselves to be sidetracked by arbitrary borders or barriers like town lines.

One tangible result of the study is that the Massachusetts Adjutant General Raymond Vezina, shortly after taking office as the head of the state's National Guard, decided to ban the practice of burning "propellant bags" on the base, a change which may set a national precedent. These bags contain the explosive charge for projectiles, and the routine had been to burn whatever was left over at the end of training "so you wouldn't let them fall into the hands of the enemy," explains General Vezina. The burn caused a great deal of smoke, the chemicals involved are considered dangerous to human health if ingested, and the BU study for the first time made a connection, noting the possibility of more cancers in residential areas near where burning took place.

Vezina is not saying that propellant-bag burns caused cancer. "We don't have those studies finished," he says. But "as an old infantry guy, I look at what they say they need for training. And this didn't make a lot of sense." In a real war, the general says, if enemy troops are so close they're about to take your propellant bags as you retreat, you're not going to stick around long enough to burn them. That thinking, coupled with the health questions, brought the change.

"So we stopped it," Vezina concludes. "Should we have stopped it a long time ago? Perhaps. And now the Army has looked at it, and said, 'What these guys in Massachusetts are doing makes sense.'"

As far as Feigenbaum is concerned, the BU study didn't focus properly, and didn't accomplish nearly enough. But it did contribute to a major change in thinking. "Probably the most important result of all the work is to establish environmental causes of cancer," he says. "Remember, when we started the BU study, the Department of Public Health was saying there weren't environmental causes of cancer, or hardly any. It was lifestyle. So the fight here has been against the establishment line that the environment does not cause cancer."

But even if people are now accepting widespread environmental catalysts for cancer, no one really understands the specific pathway, the avenue which might connect the base with its neighbors in a deadly relationship. At first, Feigenbaum and others suspected groundwater contamination, but it appears that very little contaminated water actually reached public or private wells, and regardless the plumes could not explain high rates in a full 360-degree radius. Attention then turned to airborne pollution, propellant bag burning and so forth. Yet that kind of exposure seemed too small for such a wide ranging impact. Meanwhile, other analysts like Paul Brodeur stick with the idea that invisible radiation from PAVE PAWS or electrical lines and transformers can allow cancers to grow by depressing the immune system.

In short, there is no widely accepted scientific proof of a "smoking gun," as the saying goes. And there is a growing sense that there may be more than one "smoking gun," that a combination of factors may contribute to the unusual rates of disease on Cape Cod.

Meanwhile, while the base was the focus of such work early on, it appears as though it will not be the focus of the work to come. A new grant from the state has authorized $1.5 million to be spent over the next few years looking for reasons why breast cancer is so high across Cape Cod. The head of that study, Dr. Harlee Strauss, based in Boston, says, "It's not my assumption that the base is the cause of cancer on the Cape."

Strauss sees high rates of breast and prostate cancers— an "unusual pairing," she adds, which has caused her to expand the scope of her work—in Truro, Orleans, all over the Cape. She cites "20 to 250-fold excesses" above the norm, in towns that are dozens of miles away from the base. "I just don't think (the impact of) Otis is going that far," she says.

Joel Feigenbaum argues that, in a way, the impact did indeed stretch that far. He believes that publicity about problems at the base led many Cape residents to get checked for cancer, which tended to boost figures peninsula-wide. Meanwhile, in 1986 a simple enzyme test was marketed for prostate cancer, another factor which might lead to what Feigenbaum calls "diagnostic artifacts."

Strauss suspects that there may be something real going on across the peninsula, perhaps the way our sole source aquifer (and sole source of drinking water) is affected by pollution passing through the sandy soil, which may explain what seems to be happening. She understands that Long Island, with similar geography, also has high rates of breast cancer.

"My target isn't beating up the military," Strauss concludes. "And my target isn't beating up organochlorines (in the groundwater). But I will if I need to. I'm going down whichever path leads to the answer about breast cancer."

Those are welcome words for Maryanne Waygan, a Registered Nurse who has lived most of her adult life in East Falmouth. Now 55 years old, with five children, Maryanne was diagnosed with breast cancer five years ago.

"The point is that it's real," she says. "The statistics are real. We do have an elevated cancer rate on the Cape, no ifs, ands, or buts. But we haven't taken the next step, to see what the connections are."

She doesn't know whether living near the military base was somehow the cause of her breast cancer. "Even before I was diagnosed, I was aware we live in a community affected by a Superfund site," she recalls. "You don't have to be a genius to realize that is something different than most communities." But neither is she saying she believes that is the reason. "I'm not a scientist, I'm a nurse. . . I don't have a clue what the impact is."

Working with the Cape Cod chapter of the Massachusetts Breast Cancer Coalition, Maryanne was involved in urging the state Legislature to provide money for Dr. Strauss' study. She has high hopes for the effort, but more than anything she believes in the ability of education to give the community "the power to deal with this."

Strauss' contribution to that process will not surface for years; her study, like BU's, will be complicated, exhaustive, and there is no guarantee of any better answers at the end of the road. In the meantime, Joel Feigenbaum, as usual, is agitating for a different kind of action.

"BU didn't break out females separately," he charges. "Three years have passed, now ALL they're studying is breast cancer. . . We have a political problem: what's out there right now is the perception that there's a cancer problem on the whole Cape, not the Upper Cape. And if we're looking for a cause Cape-wide, that means we're drawing attention away from the base."

Which, in an ironic way, brings us back to Terry White. Because Terry now lives in Wellfleet, his cancer shows up among the Lower Cape statistics, outside the apparent influence of the military base, and actually becomes another small statistic supporting the argument against the very connection he suspects.

But even more important to Terry, among all this uncertainty, is the fact that his concern has been left far behind: because there has been no advocate, no court action, no state office to pressure, no clearly-defined community of voters at risk, military personnel who served on the base have not been the subjects of even inconclusive investigation into whether their health has been affected.

"I really don't think you'll see anything like that happen for a hundred years, at least," he says, as he muses on the Wellfleet pier between checkups.

'The quadrangle,' Camp Edwards. November 21, 1940.

Courtesy Mass. Air National Guard.

A defunct sheep ranch becomes a city. October 10, 1940.

Underground fuel storage: out of sight, out of mind. June, 1941.

Cape Cod's oldest sewage treatment plant. January, 1941.

The guns of war on Cape Cod's dunes, World War II.

Courtesy Public Affairs Office, Camp Edwards. Photo by U.S. Army Signal Corps.

Amphibious assault on friendly shores, World War II.

Courtesy Public Affairs Office, Camp Edwards. Photo by U.S. Army Signal Corps.

Aircraft maintenance, the prop years. 1942.

Courtesy MA Air National Guard Historical Assn.

'Bier garten,' Cape Cod style, World War II.

Courtesy Public Affairs Office, Camp Edwards. Photo by U.S. Army Signal Corps.

Cold War nuclear defense: the BOMARC missile.

Courtesy Barry Donahue, Cape Cod Community Newspapers.

81

The BOMARC silos, reminders from 1960, now abandoned.

Courtesy Barry Donahue, Cape Cod Community Newspapers.

Aircraft maintenance, the jet age.

Courtesy MA Air National Guard Historical Assn.

A toxic stew of waste chemicals, dumped on the ground . . . .

Courtesy MA Air National Guard Historical Assn.

84

. . . ignited for live training. 1964.

Courtesy MA Air National Guard Historical Assn.

The legacy unearthed: barrels in the woods . . . .

Courtesy Evan Albright, Cape Cod Community Newspapers.

. . . the 'FS-12' fuel pipe in Sandwich.

Courtesy IRP Office, Mass. Military Reservation.

Courtesy Evan Albright, Cape Cod Community Newspapers.

Tying theory to reality: experimental wells containing 10,000 sampling points in the area of the sewage plume.

Courtesy IRP Office, Mass. Military Reservation.

Cleanup at 'CS-10:' pursuing the enemy within.

Soil treatment: the first source clean up at MMR.

Groundwater treatment begins: huge carbon filters at 'CS-4.'

Courtesy Matthew Cavanaugh, Cape Cod Community Newspapers.

91

Col. Ernest Keating

Dr. Joel Feigenbaum

Susan Walker

Virginia Valiela

The announcement of funding for plume containment: July 7, 1994.
Dan Santos (speaking), James Kinney (seated). . .

. . . Sen. John Kerry, Rep. Gerry Studds, Adjutant General Raymond Vezina, Sen. Edward Kennedy; Secretary of Environmental Affair Trudy Coxe.

Courtesy Paul Ott, The Falmouth Enterprise.

The main MMR landfill: 100-acre source of a 22-billion gallon plume of groundwater contamination.

Courtesy IRP Office, Mass. Military Reservation.

Firewater: A groundwater sample, taken from the area of the Sandwich pipeline, contained enough jet fuel to burn.

Courtesy Jim Richardson, Richardson Photography, Denver, CO.

99

7

MONEY, TIME, AND "THE SNAKE"

Looking at the way the federal government has responded to the crisis at Massachusetts Military Reservation, it would seem that there is virtually a limitless supply of two things: money, and time.

In the current phase of its varied life, this base has turned into a new kind of bonsai, a perfect miniature version of the wasteful, slow, redundant federal process, in which millions of tax dollars are drained into the budgets of contractors and subcontractors. Here is capsulized proof that the "military/industrial complex" which President Eisenhower warned the nation about 35 years ago not only is alive and well, but has moved into an unexpected growth area for Defense Department budgets: environmental cleanup.

The Installation Restoration Program has been extremely reluctant to surrender detailed financial information about the effort to date at the base. When even incomplete reports about how taxpayer dollars have been spent are finally released, the reason for the reluctance becomes obvious: the expenditures seem as outrageous as $200 hammers and $600 toilet seats. Meanwhile, hundreds and hundreds of studies filling tens of thousands of pieces of paper have been produced, without any clear proof that even half of them were truly necessary.

Without doubt, there has been a steep learning curve here; what needed to be explored 10 years ago is understood now; what was expensive five years ago is much cheaper now. And the federal bureaucracy, in its zeal to follow myriad protocols, forces anyone and everyone to move along an expensive trail that sometimes seems to resemble the never-ending loop of a snake biting its own tail.

Yet just as clearly, people entrusted with making sure tax dollars are carefully spent have been dozing at the switch—and that is a charitable way of describing the situation. They now admit that they cannot provide answers to the simplest, most obvious financial questions about the base cleanup to date, questions such as: How much did this study cost? How much has been spent on this particular plume? How much has that contractor been paid? What percentage goes into overhead? What percentage has been spent on actual on-site work?

In any private corporation, cost accounting as lax as this would be grounds for firing.

The detail that can be teased out from a maze of line items culled from various printouts in different formats looks a lot like the raw material of a scandal. No doubt, by Defense Department standards it is a bonsai scandal, probably so typical and small that the word would surprise people who have become numb to federal waste.

Yet figures approaching $100 million are not small potatoes by Cape Cod standards, and should be big enough to shock even the numbest. With another $250 million now in the pipeline, concern about financial oversight only deepens.

Here is the overview: from fiscal year 1985 through fiscal year 1994, roughly $96.7 million has been spent by the IRP office at the Massachusetts Military Reservation.

Of this amount, more than $80 million has been spent on studies, site investigations, fact finding, design, and other types of work, all in preparation for remediation rather than for any actual hands-on cleanup work.

From 1983 through 1993, roughly 370 studies were executed for the IRP office. This number includes various appendices and additions filed under separate covers, but does not include another 30-odd reports about various issues on the base which were funded (by and large) by other public agencies. The $96.7 million mentioned above paid for these 370 studies, among other things.

Even the most rudimentary breakdown of totals prior to 1991 is not available site by site, project by project. After 1991, financial information remains sketchy and incomplete.

The Air National Guard ($62.5 million), the Army National Guard ($30.2 million), and the United States Coast Guard ($3.9 million) all chipped in to cover the cost.

A large percentage of this work was routed through a company called HAZWRAP, which in turn hired subcontractors to handle specific jobs. HAZWRAP was involved in 285 of the 370 studies.

HAZWRAP, which stands for Hazardous Waste Remedial Actions Program, was hired through what is known as "an interagency agreement" between the Department of Defense and the Department of Energy. HAZWRAP is a subsidiary of Martin Marietta, one of the nation's biggest contractors for military hardware. In effect, Defense Department money for both weapons production and environmental cleanup has moved to the same corporation.

HAZWRAP does government work, period, and there are projects for the company in every region in the country. Yet it doesn't get its hands dirty; it does no remediation per se. HAZWRAP provides technical support, oversight, and management. It hires a variety of subcontractors to do specific jobs, such as an investigation of old records to see what might have been dumped years ago, or a site inspection to find out what is on the ground at present. This is an essential function, a crucial oversight which would be necessary in any kind of public or private situation.

Federal money to pay for this work is given to HAZWRAP, which in turn pays its subcontractors. Public officials who sign the checks say they have no veto, and no oversight, regarding the contracts which spell out exactly how much money will be spent on each job by each subcontractor.

Here is an example of how the system has worked so far: The military base needs a well dug to find out if there is pollution underground. The money will be taken from the Air National Guard's portion of the Defense Department budget for environmental cleanup, and is transferred to the Department of Energy. It then goes to HAZWRAP, which will in turn pay a subcontractor to dig the well. Every step of the way, overhead is tacked on, essentially a charge for "management," which often amounts to little more than the privilege of passing the money along. For example, the Department of Energy reportedly takes six percent of everything passing through. HAZWRAP's overhead, according to one source at the local base, is rumored to be anywhere from 10 to 40 percent for each job. Therefore, by conservative estimates, a well which might have cost $8000 with a more direct contractual agreement winds up costing roughly $15,000.

Meanwhile, to reach the point of actually digging a test well in the ground means that years have passed, and millions of dollars have already been spent.

Across the nation, all environmental efforts at Superfund sites must move through a process which is known—as most things seem to be known in this federal world—by its acronym: CERCLA. CERCLA stands for Comprehensive Environmental Response, Compensation, and Liability Act.

"The CERCLA process," explains Lorie Baker, who has been a key person for HAZWRAP working on Cape Cod, "was intended to be a scientific approach to solving a problem." What it has become, she acknowledges, is "too complicated." Others say it is not only too complicated, but too expensive, and too time consuming. They refer to the long and winding pathway as "the CERCLA snake." Under the best of circumstances, it takes years to satisfy the paper appetite of this particular reptile.

The first step, Baker explains, "is to find out what's already known. That's the records search." Documents and interviews are used to create a "preliminary assessment" which determines the scope of the problem. A draft report is generated, reviewed, and turned into a final report. That report includes some sense of whether further investigation is necessary. Usually it is.

The next step is a Site Inspection, known as an SI. HAZWRAP hires a subcontractor to look at the area in question. The SI basically tries to answer one question: is there contamination at the site? The extent of what is there is not really at issue, just a conclusive determination of whether there is something or not.

Now comes the Remedial Investigation, the RI. This is the work which figures out how big and how bad the problem has become. Detailed analysis maps the extent of the pollution. Samples of soil and water might be needed, to better understand what is really happening. A risk assessment, which addresses what kind of public health threat the site represents, is included. A draft report is reviewed and turned into a final report.

The problem has now been defined, but no solution has been proposed. Next comes the Feasibility Study, the FS. Options are identified for treatment, (as many as six to eight different approaches), and the document whittles down the choices to one or two that seem best. An FS is submitted for a mandatory public comment period, to give the community at large a chance to have a say. A draft is turned into a final report.

Next comes the Proposed Plan. This document explains what option was chosen, why, and why the others weren't as good. Once again, public comment is invited, although usually by now everyone has a pretty good sense of whether the proposed plan is going to fly or not.

At long last, as the proposed plan is finalized, there is at least a philosophical agreement about how to proceed. A Record of Decision, an RoD, formalizes that agreement. This is an official dotting of the i's and crossing of the t's. It is a summing up of the process to date, and of the decision made. It must be included as a part of the formal record; spare the RoD, spoil the project.

Notice one thing: years have passed, and nothing has yet been done to clean up pollution. And even with this Proposed Plan and the Record of Decision in hand, nothing is going to get done for many more months, or even years.

The next step is a Remedial Design, known as an RD. This document lays out the exact technical parameters for construction. It is the blueprint for work. Usually it reaches a phase in which it is "90 percent complete," as the engineers say, and then it is reviewed one last time before the finishing touches are added.

Based on the Remedial Design Document, the project is now put out to bid. This must be a public, advertised process to give every private contractor a fair chance to get the work; it cannot be rushed. The bids received are opened, compared, and one company wins. The losers have the right to protest, and have the decision reviewed.

Once all that is accomplished, there is an event which is known as the RA. This is the Remedial Action, or the Removal Action. Translated, this is the moment at which something actually changes in the environment, when an attack on contamination is attempted. It might be an Interim RA, which won't solve the problem but will improve the situation. Regardless, this is the moment we've all been waiting for.

There is a reason to all this, a method to what some see as a bureaucratic form of madness: cumbersome as it is, this process is meant to ensure that public dollars are spent wisely, that no quick decisions are made that would benefit private parties.

Yet the result of this clumsy, careful, halting process is that speed is a casualty. Each step takes time—lots of time.

It is true that sometimes several steps can be taken simultaneously; for instance, a Proposed Plan and planning for a Remedial Design can move forward side by side. Even so, durations of years would still be considered "fast track" to get to treatment. Ten years would be considered a "straight line."

And the money involved in this process is incredible. For starters, let's take one small example:

Since the beginning of work on the Cape military base, investigators have known that there are dry wells, known as sumps, which are located all over the area. These sumps were usually little more than holes in the ground, catch basins, some with concrete sides, used to hold anything and everything that drained off places that were paved. Hangars had sumps, workshops had sumps. Fuel and oil and hydraulics often were hosed off the floor into drains which led to these holes, where the liquid slowly seeped into the ground.

Site by site, records searches and digging around revealed these sumps. Some were still active, others disconnected. Some obviously received a great deal of pollution and clearly were the cause of underground problems. Others seemed more benign. Clearly, digging the dangerous ones up, stopping whatever seepage could still be stopped, and cleaning up in the surrounding area was an important part of the "installation restoration."

At first glance, it would also seem to be one of the easier things to do. After all, the sumps were obvious, they were small, their structures were simple and contained. On the other hand, there were a lot of them; over 200 were found, and roughly 170 looked like they should be removed.

Early investigation of these structures was folded into site work at much of the base. Based on those findings, work on a handful of the foulest of these dry wells was done around 1990; some floating liquid was removed. But according to financial records at the base, widespread work on sumps wasn't begun until 1991 or 1992.

In June, 1992, HAZWRAP and one of its favorite subcontractors, ABB Environmental Services, released four parts of a "draft work completion report." This was a "Phase 1 Sump Investigation Program," examining approximately 100 sumps. "This phase evaluated the nature and extent of contamination at the sites." The report was accompanied by six appendices.

Four months later, the draft was released as a "Final Work Completion Report."

Two months later, a "Draft Statement of Work for Phase II Sump Investigations" was published.

One month later, a "Final Work Plan, Phase II Sump Investigations," this time by Metcalf & Eddy, another subcontractor under HAZWRAP, was submitted. "This plan will document the National Guard Bureau's planned Phase II investigation of 15 Priority 1 sump sites at the MMR."

Nine months later, a "Draft Site Investigation Report, Priority 2 and 3 Study Areas" was released by ABB Environmental Services and HAZWRAP. Included in this was a volume with "information on sump and dry well construction."

Through 1993, this is the full extent of the reported material about sumps, according to a list provided by the IRP office which supposedly lists all published work on the military base through 1993. And as of August, 1994, no removal action on any of these sumps being investigated had been done. None is planned until fiscal year 1995; the remedial design is expected to be submitted in fiscal year 1994.

Here is the shocker: according to internal financial documents, in 1992 the Army National Guard paid $1,700,000 into the project whose sole purpose was "basewide sump investigation." In 1993, the Army National Guard paid another $1,064,000 for this same project. For just these two years, the Army National Guard's total spent was $2,764,000.

And that's not all. These same internal documents show that the Army National Guard is paying for only a portion of the total sump work to date. While the Air National Guard is the lead agency handling the cleanup as a whole, each branch of the armed services pays a percentage based roughly on how much responsibility each bears for the pollution. That figure varies from site to site; in this case, the Army National Guard's portion is 45 percent. Base accountant Beth Terrien confirms that this figure represents 45 percent of the money spent on sump investigations during these two years. Therefore, the total for 1992 and 1993 comes in at $6,142,222.

Keep in mind that not a single one of these sumps has been removed. A Remedial Design isn't even approved. Yet in two years alone, more than $6.1

million has been spent in the process. This figure does not include any work done prior to 1992, for which no accounting has been provided.

"We're now at 90 percent of design to go remove those things," says HAZWRAP's Lorie Baker. "There's a lot of these on the base. You can't remove the active ones. It's a complicated process."

"Remember, the entire base had to be surveyed," explains Tom Noble from the local IRP office.

Perhaps the many locations of sumps makes this example unusual, if not unfair. Let's take another, this time for one of the few sites where real cleanup has begun.

CS-4, known as the West Truck Motor Pool, is the source of the long, thin plume which is moving south off the base under the Crane Wildlife Refuge. People have known about contamination at this site since the early 1980s, if not earlier; the site was discussed in the earliest fact-finding reports in 1983 and 1986.

The first HAZWRAP study which singles out CS-4 for detailed work was released in June, 1990, as a "Draft Focused Feasibility Study." By this time, researchers knew they would have to treat soil and groundwater separately. This study looked only at soils.

Four months later, a companion draft study on groundwater was issued. By May and June of 1991, draft statements of work and engineering evaluations were coming forward. In August, draft remedial designs appeared, followed by a public comment period (which was distilled into a report). In November, 1991, a groundwater treatment proposal appeared in draft, followed by an action memorandum, a responsiveness summary, and a 90 percent design for soil treatment.

This list goes on and on; the number of reports reached 31. Finally, in May, 1992, a Record of Decision was reached: groundwater would be pulled up in wells at the toe of the plume, and treated. In July, a system design was submitted. Construction could begin to move forward.

The full cost of this project, including research and treatment, cannot accurately be generated, according to federal officials both locally and in Washington DC. Why not? Gary Hinkle, who manages the national IRP program for the Air National Guard, explains:

"When we fund things, we put together a program, we lump sites together that will undergo the same effort of work. . . We don't keep a clear accounting of what each site costs. We keep estimates, but they're almost worthless."

For example, Hinkle continues, there may be work in progress on 10 sites at the Massachusetts Military Reservation. Each one needs remedial investigation. HAZWRAP is handling them all, and subcontracting work to various other businesses. Hinkle gives HAZWRAP a lump sum—and that's the end of the accounting. As Hinkle puts it, he might say to HAZWRAP, "Here: this $100,000 will get you through your field effort." And that's about it.

Not only are projects on Cape Cod lumped together, but Cape Cod sometimes has been included with HAZWRAP projects in other parts of the country. Ask Hinkle how much money HAZWRAP has been paid for work to date on Cape Cod, and he answers, "That's a wonderful question. I don't have a breakdown on that."

The money paid to HAZWRAP does not necessarily stay there; much of it goes to subcontractors hired for specific jobs. When Hinkle is asked how much of the money is passed along, and how much is kept by HAZWRAP, he says he has no idea about that either.

"HAZWRAP gets to do the negotiations (with their subcontractors), and we're not privy to the negotiations," he explains. "But then they'd come to us for the money."

And so, as far as CS-4 is concerned, there are only a few, unsatisfying things we can say about the money spent. Financial documents show that from 1991 through 1993, $1,228,000 was kicked in by the Army National Guard on the "planning phase." Obviously, work on this site had been contracted before 1991, but those figures are not available. Meanwhile, another $441,000 was paid in 1992 for "soil remediation." For the three years from 1992 through 1994, another $1,759,000 was paid for "interim groundwater containment."

Thirty-one studies, more than $3 million since 1991 alone. All this for what is considered to be a small, simple plume, for what has been characterized as a major success for the local IRP office, a real "fast-track" to a treatment facility that actually does something, that people actually can see.

"And CS-4 is a pinprick compared to the others," says Dan Santos, former head of the cleanup program at the base:

At the BOMARC area, the Army National Guard has spent $3,338,000 from 1991 through 1994; no removal action is planned until fiscal year 1995 at the earliest, and estimates are that as much as $77.5 million will be needed between now and the turn of the century to pay for various remedial actions.

At a small pesticide shop, where chemicals spilled into the ground, $108,000 was spent in 1991 and 1992 to look into the problem and sample the soil. No action to remove the pollution is expected until April, 1995, at the earliest.

In the Impact Area, an anonymous caller tipped off the IRP office that there is an acre or so of land which is bare—nothing grows on it. Over $180,000 has been spent since 1992 looking at the "bald acre," as it has been nicknamed. So far, there isn't even enough information to know if the ground is contaminated or not. Field work will continue in 1995.

An 11,000-gallon fuel spill from an old tank has been studied. The spill has been confirmed. No work has been done on the problem, and no design for work is expected until 1996. Even so, $480,000 has been obligated for the area since 1991.

Another underground storage tank which reportedly leaked years ago needs work. A remedial investigation is due this year. Just to reach this point, to finish the investigations, will cost about $525,000.

"Site investigation for two or three small sites is running close to $200,000," says Gary Hinkle. "I'd say $100,000 of that is for sampling." By sampling, Hinkle means drilling a type of well which is capable of sending up a dozen or more samples from different depths underground. Each sample must be tested, to see exactly where the plumes have reached.

Hinkle's "guesstimate" seems low, but there is no way to be precise, no way to break out exactly why each project has cost as much as it has, or even exactly how much of this money has moved through HAZWRAP. To give a sense of how shoddy the accounting seems to be, consider another example:

Air National Guard financial reports show that HAZWRAP received $2.5 million from that branch of the military in 1991. $400,000 was directed toward work on the landfill; the exact nature of the work is not specified, but at least we have a location. The remaining $2.1 million is shown, with no more detail, as going to the following sites: a fire training area, the landfill, a storm drainage disposal site, the west truck motor pool, a former refueler maintenance shop motor pool, BOMARC, a railroad fuel pumping station, an aquafarm area, and the range E-3 spill.

As Gary Hinkle suggests, to look for totals of HAZWRAP funding for the Massachusetts base is to enter a labyrinth of documents with muddled paper trails for maps. The best estimate is that the three branches of the military (Air National Guard, Army National Guard, and Coast Guard) have combined to send HAZWRAP more than $40 million in recent years. HAZWRAP in turn sends a good deal of that money to its subcontractors, but there is no accounting available to the public which shows how much.

Tom Noble, a hydrologist who works for the IRP program at the military base and manages a number of the cleanup sites, says he has heard "rumors" about HAZWRAP's overhead which range from "10 to 40 percent." Using a $40 million total figure, 10 percent would be $4 million; 40 percent would mean $16 million off the top.

Denis LeBlanc from the US Geological Survey understands what it really means to do field work, to spend money to get results. He also has watched this process very carefully.

"A frighteningly large amount of money gets spent on things that don't put holes in the ground, and don't answer questions," LeBlanc says. "Up to this point, the priority has been to map the plumes. So it would be reasonable to ask, 'How much of these dollars have been spent to pay people to drill wells and plot the plumes?' My impression is that if they say more than 25 percent, they're lying."

Until recently, Dan Santos was in charge of the local IRP office. His responsibilities included financial oversight. Yet, says Santos, he never was able to put a clear accounting system in place. The structure of the IRP program, he maintains, never allowed that to happen.

"You could hire an army of auditors, and still have trouble figuring out how the money was spent," Santos continues. "And that fact opened it up to waste. There's too much skimming going on—legally. And too much overhead every step of the way."

Santos claims that on several occasions he asked the Department of Energy (the agency which oversees the contract with HAZWRAP) to audit the company, because the amount of money being billed seemed high. "The DoE said that the audits kept coming back clean," says Santos. "But how can that be? How can you be walking in the mud and come back clean?"

Hinkle says that at least one audit did indeed turn up problems. About two years ago, Hinkle reveals, the Secretary of the Air Force called for an audit of HAZWRAP: "He was concerned. It was costing us more to work through HAZWRAP than handle the situations ourselves."

Did the audit show problems with spending? "Yes it did," Hinkle says. "And there were other concerns: that HAZWRAP was calling the shots for Uncle Sam."

As a small example, Hinkle remembers the audit focusing on HAZWRAP's handling of a student intern program for the IRP office. According to Hinkle, a student in the program, brought in to work on cleanup at a military base, would be paid $24,000 for an entry level position. Yet HAZWRAP was being paid $55,000 per student by the government. In this case, apparently, the management charge was $31,000—$7000 more than the student's salary. That translates into an overhead of 116 percent.

The audit suggested that the Air Force use its own, in-house intern program to get students. And here, adds Hinkle, is the irony: he did that, he applied for four positions, and when his budget came back after going through the long review process, "You know what I got? Nothing."

But that doesn't excuse the financial excess. "When you have somebody else manage a project for you, you're at their mercy," says Hinkle. "But we had no choice."

That employers are at "the mercy" of the managers they hire would come as a surprise to many. Regardless, Hinkle says that the reason the federal government had "no choice" in the matter is because the environmental cleanup programs around the country were in their infancy. There wasn't a solid group of managers in place to handle their own operations. Now that the IRP office at Massachusetts Military is more "mature," to use Hinkle's term, local staff can take more of the load.

Lorie Baker from HAZWRAP is not in a position within the company to account for the money spent, but she does understand the work. "The entire environmental industry has evolved so much in this time," she explains. "We had to go through what we went through in order to arrive at where we are now. It's been an evolution. I think everybody would tell you that."

When HAZWRAP first started work on the base, fundamental technology like the screened augur well (which allows investigators to take many water samples from many levels with just one well) was not widely used. The research and experimentation that needed to be done was very costly, and time-consuming. "From the public point of view, God, it takes so long," she agrees. "But people really are busy all this time."

"We started with an industry in its infancy, and here we are now," says Dan

Santos. "Yeah, we wasted a lot of money. But it was trial and error. In 1983 we didn't know what we were doing."

Ron Watson, former head of the IRP program for the Air National Guard, calls the early investigations "kind of a roll of the dice. You'd put two wells below and one above and hope you were in the plume. The knowledge we have now allows us to do Monday morning quarterbacking."

Baker adds that the CERCLA process, the federal hoops that need to be jumped through, represents an outrageous obstacle course. "Sometimes it's just amazing to me that we progress at all, given all the requirements," she says.

If the professionals were frustrated, the community around the base was outraged. "We kept saying, $15 million and you haven't put a shovel in,'" remembers Susan Walker. "It was pretty pathetic."

"I'm damn glad you guys weren't over at Desert Storm," Juan Bacigalupi (who in fact did serve in Desert Storm) told local military officials. "It took us six months to launch an invasion. It's taking us 25 years to stop these plumes."

But in truth, we have spent the last 25 years in a state of perpetual military readiness, spending billions of dollars a year to make sure we can launch an invasion in six months, if necessary. There has been no comparable commitment to environmental issues; the last 10 years at the Massachusetts Military Reservation, some say, have been spent trying to get up to speed.

"It's easy to say, 'There's stuff in the ground, we have to get it out,'" says Lorie Baker. "But how do you do it? You need information to know that."

Unfortunately, additional information about the specifics of money spent at the base are not available. Repeated efforts to contact someone at HAZWRAP who could provide more detail were unsuccessful. Local military base officials indicated that either they did not know any more specifics, or were not authorized to provide such information.

As far as this base is concerned, Pentagon funding is about to move in a new direction. According to Hinkle, HAZWRAP is being phased out of the process. Local staff will handle some of their work, while Stone and Webster, another large corporation with extensive Defense Department contacts, is going to take control of much of the big contracting work coming up.

Does this mean that HAZWRAP is being fired? "Basically," says Hinkle. "From 1985 until now, these environmental firms have been making a killing.

Now, when everyone sees how lucrative it is, they're all getting into it. And it's more and more competitive."

Hinkle's implication is that a change of contractors will go a long way toward solving problems many people now admit exist. Yet there is no clear reason why that would be the case. The process is no different; only the name has been changed. There is no guarantee that the oversight will be any tighter, that the quality of the "mercy" which Hinkle says he relies upon will be any better.

Ron Watson has seen similar situations base by base, state by state. He says that the local case is not some kind of unique or outrageous example. "The dollars spent up there is not a high number nationally," says Watson. "It's probably a low number for investigative work. . . And I have a gut feeling that Otis has gone pretty much in a straight line from investigation to treatment. Others haven't really gone that way."

The most charitable way of describing what is a very disturbing situation is Watson's: "The government paid people to learn how to do studies. Now the government has to pay people to learn how to clean up."

Joel Feigenbaum's analysis says that the cumbersome process and lack of expertise are not at the root of the problem. "A lot of this is just to spend money," he says. "You've got to understand that. It's not cleanup. It's a conversion of wartime spending for what are called environmental activities, funded through the Pentagon."

"This is the new version of the military/industrial complex," says Mark Forest, US Congressman Gerry Studds' point man on Cape Cod. "And if this is how this one site is managed, imagine what's going on with the thousands of others."

8

ON THE GROUND

Millions of gallons of water polluted, millions of dollars spent.

Those two facts suggest a crucial message: if we can't truly clean up after ourselves, then the only common sense thing to say is that we really shouldn't do it in the first place.

That simple sentence translates into extremely difficult decisions for a prosperous society which relies on landfills, incinerators, and septic systems—not to mention cars, factories, and nuclear power plants. Yet it remains the fundamental lesson of the Massachusetts Military Reservation.

Unfortunately, as the old saying goes, the horse already is out of the barn. We can't go back in time and erase a catastrophe in the making, nor can we simply sit and wait for the future to offer some miraculous cure. We have to confront an overwhelming problem with the resources now at hand.

Given a decade, and more than $80 million worth of studies and preparation, the actual in-the-ground, up-and-running treatment facilities at the military base might not seem like too much bang for the buck. Yet the modest efforts that exist, and the ambitious project in the works, stand as snapshots of what is the international state of the art when it comes to treating groundwater pollution.

So far, treatment has amounted to schemes that bear a disquieting resemblance to Rube Goldberg inventions: miles of pipes running to and from a central unit like webs off a huge spider, extraction and injections wells buried like underground picket fences, an oven like a huge pottery kiln to bake dirt, tanks holding tons of carbon to filter water, a gigantic cap of clay and plastic meant to keep the rain off dozens of acres of garbage.

And there are other approaches in the works, some tried elsewhere, some so far out on the cutting edge that this will be their test ground: bacteria genetically engineered to eat petroleum might munch through the fuel. Air forced into the ground like someone blowing on a straw into the bottom of a glass of Coke might bubble up pollution now trapped below. A pipe filled with little more than rusty iron filings, believe it or not, might catch and hold dangerous solvents.

Amid all the nuts and bolts, emerging from the theories, there is a very sobering realization: given what we know today, given hundreds of millions of dollars, we cannot clean up the groundwater seeping out of the military base. The best we can do, so far, is try to contain these plumes. If the huge treatment facility now funded (but still years away from operation) works perfectly, exactly as planned, the area where billions of gallons of water have been contaminated will not become clean. Water coursing through it for decades to come will be polluted much as it has been in decades past. If everything goes perfectly, all we will be able to say is that the plumes of contamination have not grown larger still.

A future generation may look back on these technological efforts with some bemusement and some respect, perhaps like we now regard the Wright brothers and their crude airplane. Hopefully, they won't think of these efforts as so much snake oil.

For Ed Pesce, project engineer for the remediation project at the base, the big picture of work translates into engineering detail, in the execution of designs. He was hired near the beginning of 1992, and the first cleanup he got going was what is known as a "pump and treat" system for the CS-4 plume.

CS-4 is a long, narrow plume which was made mainly by years of dumping oils and solvents out the back door of one of the base's service areas for trucks and other machinery. It has moved off the base, under the Crane Wildlife Sanctuary, and was threatening the Coonamessett Pond neighborhood of Falmouth.

As Pesce explains, beginning in October, 1992, the following system was built:

Thirteen wells were dug about 140 feet into the ground, in an area downstream from the farthest point the plume had reached so far. Each pump feeds a stainless steel pipe six inches in diameter. The wells were placed in a line 800 feet long, and each well was built so it could capture water from a 35-foot-wide area underground. Each pump is powerful enough to pull as much as 20 gallons per minute.

All these specifications have a point: to capture every drop of the polluted water. According to all the studies, the plume itself is no more than 700 feet wide, less than 35 feet thick. Twenty-nine monitoring wells have been drilled behind and around the "fence" to make sure no contaminated water has snuck through. If it has, new wells would have to be dug—and hundreds of thousands of dollars worth of study and design would be flawed. Once the water is pumped up, it moves through eight-inch pipe 5300 feet (almost exactly a mile) to the treatment facility. The pipe is double walled for greater protection. "Every 300 feet there's a manhole, with gauges which tell us if there's a leak in the line," Pesce explains.

The water passes into a small building where there are two of what Ed calls "10,000-pound carbon contact units." The carbon, like charcoal, is a filter which is very effective at catching the kind of pollution found in the CS-4 plume, such as chlorinated solvents which were used to clean machinery. Periodically the carbon filters have to be washed, changed, or revived; the second filter on site helps ensure constant treatment. Meanwhile, computers monitor the pumps and the flow, to make sure everything is working.

When the water passes out of the treatment tanks it should be clean enough to drink, but even so, it goes back into the ground. Gravity carries it into several long leaching trenches which return the water close to the treatment unit (upstream from the "fence" where it came from). If the groundwater wasn't allowed to seep back, and enough of it was pumped out to begin with, the area's water table could be changed—affecting such things as the height of local ponds.

The system is up and running, although its success cannot be measured until the plume reaches the fence and real treatment begins, probably in 1995. Changes in design, like having to move one well which couldn't be drilled properly, drove the cost of the project to about $2 million, up from an estimated $1.6 million.

The most daunting fact of all about this way of attacking pollution is the time involved: not only does the system have to be working 24 hours a day, 365 days a year, but it has to remain in place for decades. It will take that long before all the chemicals now underground find their way through the soil to the groundwater, head downstream to the fence, and then are removed by the filters.

This was chosen to be the first area treated partly because this plume was a threat to homes, and partly because it is narrow and focused, pencil-shaped, which means the fence of wells to stop it could be shorter (and cheaper). The hope is that this smaller version will serve as a model for a giant cousin soon to be built, and that the manageable size would minimize complications and surprises.

But, as Ed Pesce reports, there was at least one unexpected jolt: as tests of water in the area came back, another chemical, ethylenedibromide (EDB), was found much deeper underground, below where CS-4 is located. "It was very deep, and it was a surprise," Pesce acknowledges. "It could be an old spill from somewhere else, it could be something long gone by, we don't really know."

The levels are very low, but even tiny amounts of EDB are dangerous for human consumption. No plan has yet come forward for treatment. In the meantime, the pump and treat system is in place, ready to do its job—but there may be other contaminants too deep for its fence to reach, outside the scope of its design.

Up near the head of the CS-4 plume, another technology is trying to attack some of the "hottest," most contaminated soils on the base. Its official name is a "low-temperature thermal desorption unit." The mission is to treat nearly 20,000 cubic yards of dirt, which translates to 31,000 tons.

The dirt is coming mainly from three sources: the maintenance yard that created the CS-4 plume, the fire training area where any kind of oil or chemical that would light was dumped on the ground, and a refueling area for tankers where diesel was spilled.

"The idea is to aerate the soil in an oven-type situation," Pesce explains. The dirt passes up a conveyor belt and moves into a kiln, a baking oven set at 180 degrees Fahrenheit. In this case, the recipe calls for the fuel and solvents bound up in the dirt to turn into gases. Provided it is properly cooked, the soil should now be clean, ready to be hauled back to where it came from. A test double-checks the process.

The hot air then passes through a "particulate bag house," which screens out anything solid on the way into what looks like two big dumpsters. The dumpsters have another type of carbon filter in them, this time designed to remove compounds from air rather than water. In many ways they are meant to act like huge versions of the old "charcoal-filtered" cigarettes.

Base officials had not expected to use this kind of filter. They had been planning on "venting" the hot air drawn off the soil, running it through a big version of the catalytic converter found in the exhaust systems of cars. But vociferous opposition to that idea surfaced among community groups who didn't want to trade pollution in the ground for possible pollution in the air. After hundreds of letters objecting to the idea, and a series of tense negotiations between the IRP office and citizen activists, the carbon filter option was chosen.

The cost of this thermal treatment is about $2.7 million, and it is expected to take five months to process all the dirt. Pesce has added a few more "hot spots" for treatment: a fuel disposal pipeline near the old railroad yard, several locations in the block of World War II buildings that have been torn down or abandoned, another spot near the commissary. All have pockets of contaminated soil, and all could benefit from a bake in the oven.

Then there is the granddaddy of the first phase of remediation, the attempt to cap the base's giant landfill. Begun in the summer of 1993, this effort is expected to take two years and cost $8 million. Landfill caps are going on all over the Cape, the state, and the country, but this one is unusual because of its size: 60 acres will be covered.

Actually, the landfill extended 100 acres, and was divided into a series of "cells" which were filled up and then closed at various points through the past 60 years. "Three of the old cells are not being capped," says Pesce, because studies to date show "they are not acting as contamination for groundwater."

The three oldest cells were shut down in 1947, 1951, and 1957. The three newer cells, along with a disposal trench, seem to be the focus of the huge plume seeping west into Bourne.

For all of these 60 acres, the idea is the same: lay a multilayer protection, a kind of roof, over the site. The goal is to stop any rainwater from seeping into the ground and hastening the flow of what everyone admits is a wide variety of toxic substances now buried, everything from oils and hydraulics to gunpowder, battery acid—you name it.

The first layer is a cap of synthetic clay. Since most things in these sorts of projects must have acronyms, this one is known as the "GCL," the geosynthetic clay liner.

On top of the liner comes a layer of polyethylene plastic 20 mils thick. It looks more like a tough tar shingle than a black plastic garbage bag, the equivalent of a thick tarp.

"The plastic is supposed to be impervious," says Pesce, "and shed water. But if there is a tear, or a rip, the water hits the clay below which swells and seals the hole."

Laying this material is painstaking work, done foot by foot. Before the project is done, a million cubic yards of soil will have been moved, an amount impossible to comprehend. What once was the dump will look like a large, gently sloping mound, a big grassy hill. The plastic will be covered by grass planted on a layer of sand two and a half feet thick, a buffer meant to protect the liner.

The hill will have a placid look, but it will be hiding a cauldron of poison. The cap should retard the spread of this material, but it will in no way clean or remove any of it. Included in the stew are barrels of hazardous waste, an uncounted number of drums filled with unidentified liquids. Pesce admits that these barrels "may rupture and leak. There is 60 feet of sand between them and groundwater. How significant will that problem be? That's arguable."

Actually, even basic information like the distance between the pollution and the groundwater is arguable. Pesce says 60 feet, but in some areas the buffer may be as little as 15 feet. That information led some to argue that capping the landfill is not good enough. "Covering up the landfill is not a solution," read a leaflet written by an alliance of concerned citizens several years ago. "Toxic wastes buried there will eventually leach into the groundwater, cap or no cap."

"Will they leak?" Pesce asks rhetorically, speaking of the buried barrels. "You can't say they won't. Will it be a problem? You can't say it will."

Meanwhile, he adds, given the types and amounts of waste, "excavation and disposal would be cost prohibitive. . . We didn't have a billion dollars to treat this as hazardous waste."

Lorie Baker from HAZWRAP adds another factor: "You need to look at the risks you're exposing the workers to. Putting materials in a truck, hauling hazardous materials off-base, this is all dangerous work. And these cells are very large, and very deep."

Baker adds that "capping" has been the chosen method of trying to reduce damage caused by landfills across the country. Many towns are faced with the same problem—what has been dumped over the decades is too extensive and dangerous to clean out, so the next best thing to do is try to seal it off. But most towns probably do not have to consider the extraordinary amounts of chemicals associated with military refuse. "All kinds of military bases did the exact same thing," she notes. "And industrial landfills will be even worse."

Northeast of the landfill, where the old Sandwich pipeline ruptured and sent tens of thousands of gallons of fuel into the ground, an entirely different first approach was taken. Engineers thought they had a shot at a real cleanup, done real quick: it looked like there was a literal lake of fuel floating above the groundwater, 90 feet or so underground. As we all know, oil and water don't mix; it appeared that as much as 30,000 gallons of free-floating petroleum might be sucked up and removed if a pair of wells could be drilled into the right spot. "Free product recovery," the technique is called.

With high hopes, an experiment went forward in the fall of 1993. Unfortunately, as Evan Albright reported in *The Register* newspaper in late September, "A test of the pumping system last week failed to bring even one gallon of fuel to the surface."

To this day, people are not sure why the test failed. One theory, mentioned by Bob Kreykenbohm from the Sandwich Water District, is that heavy rains earlier that year (after years of little rainfall) might have lifted the water table and "smudged" the lake. Another theory is that the lake is more illusion than fact, that the fuel really is bound up in dirt and is not floating free.

Either way, reports Ed Pesce, the treatment of choice has become "air sparging." Wells are drilled into the groundwater, but instead of drawing water out, these wells pump air down. The air then naturally bubbles up—like bubbles from a straw at the bottom of a glass of Coke. Fuel vapor is carried up by the rising air and is drawn off at the surface. Pesce hopes to have a contractor chosen and construction underway before the end of 1994, more than a year after the first try failed.

Meanwhile, several intriguing alternatives are in the mix of ideas presently being considered to try to do more than stop these plumes, or treat a single "hot spot." If there is hope for the future, it may lie in one of these two approaches:

"Bioremediation" is a fancy term for a fundamental fact of life: there are some bugs which love to eat carbon. Fuel is a carbon source, which means it could be food for these little microbes. The idea is to find the right kind of bacteria for the particular kind of pollution (there are biotech companies right now genetically engineering life forms to fit the bill), and then create an environment in the plume that will encourage these bugs to eat up whatever is there. The pollution is transformed by this natural process into basic, harmless things like water and carbon dioxide.

"Pick a waste stream, they've got a microbe for it," says Ed Pesce. "They're called 'facultative bacteria,' and they'll eat BTEX (a combination of fuel components), nitrogen, and hydrocarbon."

Many of these organisms need oxygen, which is in short supply deep underground. This is one of the technical hurdles to overcome with bioremediation. Other questions have to do with efficiency, whether this method will clean water to the pure levels needed for safe drinking. And there's always the possibility that some genetically engineered microbe could affect the environment in ways we can't even imagine, let alone predict.

The great benefit, of course, is that nature's help is much cheaper than running pumps and filters 24 hours a day for years. And bacteria can target right on concentrations of pollution anywhere they are found, rather than waiting until the plume reaches a line of defense to begin treatment.

There has been enough field work to say that this is no test tube fantasy. "This process is becoming more and more accepted," Pesce reports. "For a ma and pa gas station, it's probably a great alternative."

It appears that without our help, bacteria have been eating away at one of the plumes which is in the Ashumet Pond area. Pesce is expecting to run some tests to try to understand what is happening and how the natural process might be made even more effective. For instance, some initial studies suggest that a combination of more oxygen, and a more acidic environment, could break down solvents and leave only harmless byproducts.

Meanwhile, experimental hardware approaches are moving forward as well. The base is also about to become the site of "the first full-scale test in the world," says Pesce, which could "revolutionize the way we treat porous media spills." The technique to be tested in one part of the fire training spill has been dubbed "the magic sand" approach, an appropriate term because the process feels almost like some form of alchemy.

According to Pesce, iron filings, typically rusty old scraps of discarded machinery, have a natural positive charge which draws and holds negatively-charged material. Chemicals of the chlorine family, for instance, have a negative charge, and also happen to be one of the most common and dangerous forms of industrial pollution. And so the idea is to expose the water in the plume to a gauntlet of iron filings.

To do that, an experimental wall of steel sheets will be driven deep into the ground, just like a typical fence above ground, but buried deep enough so that it will stop groundwater. The fence will be shaped in a V pattern to funnel water toward the point of the V. At the point, a long pipe filled with these iron filings, buried about 100 feet below the surface, will catch the water. If the filings do what they're supposed to, water coming out the far end of the pipe will be clean—and the filings should remain viable for as long as a decade.

"Operation and management costs are almost completely eliminated," says Pesce.

Whether "magic sand" can eliminate all the dangerous compounds underground remains to be seen. In the meantime, more conventional technology has been chosen to begin one of the biggest public works projects in Cape Cod history: a multi-plume cleanup.

After all the discussions and studies, by the spring of 1994 there was agreement that seven plumes should be stopped. The best way to do that, a team of consultants concluded, is to build what they call a "CTU," a central treatment unit. This facility would receive contaminated water from all seven plumes, treat it all, and send it back into the ground. In essence, it would be a giant version of what already has been installed for the single CS-4 plume.

This system is a high-tech, high-maintenance attempt to solve seven problems at once. It was proposed as a way to save money and time, to focus effort on one facility. It puts all the cleanup eggs in one huge basket, with one huge price tag: over $100 million for construction, and another $150 million for operation and maintenance over the course of the next 20 years.

Just as with the small "pump and treat" system in place, "fences" of wells will be dug below the toes of all seven plumes now identified. To give a sense of the scope of this project, consider these figures:

The landfill plume in Bourne will need 33 extraction wells located in two fences, covering 4600 feet.

The BOMARC plume will need 43 extraction wells spread across 2800 feet in two lines.

The Sandwich pipeline plume will need 14 extraction wells spread over 2200 feet.

All told, there will be 458 extraction wells, which will be pumping nearly 8000 gallons of water every minute of every day into this Central Treatment

Unit. A computer on site will monitor thousands of sensors, meant to reveal problems that can crop up anywhere in the system, from a leak to a freeze to a breakdown. A 100,000-gallon tank will hold water waiting to be treated. Once again, huge carbon tanks will handle the bulk of the filter work; 15 of them will be in place, each holding 10 tons of carbon. Double-walled pipes will carry water from beyond the base and within the base, running for miles in every direction. Pipes will also carry the water back not far from its starting point, because to draw this much water out of the ground and not replace most of it would dramatically change the whole region's groundwater flow.

The system's complexity borders on the incredible. There are centrifugal pumps and manifolds, flow indicators and leak detectors, pressure switches and filter presses, extraction lines injection lines and backwash lines, computer dial-in ports and modems, automatic control and manual overrides. Two people will have to be present at all times—for at least 20 years. Because so much of the pollution has moved off the base, wells and pipes will have to be placed in the surrounding communities; exactly where is still not clear, but the construction is bound to disrupt many lives for a long time.

Under the best of circumstances, something like this is not built overnight; as we have seen, the federal process which controls this kind of construction is not the best of circumstances. Even with pressure to speed up as much as possible, Dan Santos says that "the first plume treatment will probably begin in three years," meaning three years after the contracting process begins. He does not expect the whole system to be up and running for another six months after that. Three and a half years, he adds, is probably two to three years faster than the typical time frame.

Given the present schedule, construction on the system wouldn't begin until March, 1996. The first actual treatment of groundwater wouldn't begin until a year later.

"That is unacceptable," says Joel Feigenbaum. "We don't think that's fast enough," agrees Eileen Gunn, speaking for the Coalition for Buzzards Bay.

"We've only taken two years off of a six-year process," says Susan Nickerson from APCC. "We want to take at least another year off, to cut it in half."

"It may even be a fatal flaw," adds George Seaver. His main concern is the landfill plume, which by mid-1994 seemed poised to pollute two of Bourne's public wells within 18 months. If the system is not ready for four years, says Seaver, "then the containment wells will have to be put 100 feet out in

Megansett Harbor."

Even in Washington, the imminent threat from the landfill plume was recognized during debate about funding. "I was given direction to come up with a feasible technical plan to preserve the water supply in Bourne," Santos reported in July, 1994. Plans called for a "carbon filtration unit" to be attached directly to the public supply wells. But experts, officials and concerned citizens feared the precedent of the military treating water at the wellhead instead of cleaning up the aquifer. After they questioned the wisdom of the approach, base authorities have now agreed to search for new, uncontaminated supplies for Bourne.

What is clear is that staggering amounts of money are involved. Although all the funding will come from federal tax dollars, consultants who came up with the cost estimates refused to reveal exactly how they arrived at their figures. To do so, they argued, would jeopardize the competitive bidding process which will choose a contractor; if the contractors all see the estimates, they will tailor their bids accordingly.

Regardless, the proposal on the table supposedly will cost $102.2 million to build. That figure is broken down plume by plume: $23.6 million for Ashumet Valley, $14.3 million for the landfill, $16.8 million for BOMARC, and so forth. The central treatment unit will supposedly cost $23.6 million.

And that's just the beginning. To operate the plant, to test the treated water, to repair and change parts and filters, all will cost what look like big bucks. Over the course of 20 years, estimates show steadily rising maintenance fees, from $4.5 million for the first year of operation to $11.3 million the last year. The grand total for 20 years is more than $150 million— and two decades most likely is not a long enough time to guarantee that the plumes will be gone.

How did the engineers arrive at these estimates? According to their own report, they took the first year of operation, figured a cost, and then added "a 4.9 percent escalation factor" for every single year thereafter. By the 20th year, annual maintenance was over $11 million.

"Some people are going to make a lot of money," says Al Orlando, whose work in the Briarwood area led him to become one of Mashpee's water commissioners. "But I suppose it's better for them to be making money like this than by building missiles."

Dan Santos believes that the actual bids to build and run the system will come in well under these initial estimates. Let's hope so; every project on the ground so far has wound up costing more than the accepted bid stated, a common malady for large construction projects.

Remember, this $250 million will not clean up the contamination. It will stop the leading edges of these plumes. Exactly where that edge is found depends on how quickly the containment wells are put in place; the longer it takes, the farther away the wells must be, the longer the connecting pipes must be, and the more water is polluted in between.

All that said, the money spent at Cape Cod's Superfund site hopefully will do more than stop the spread of these plumes: technology tested here could help hundreds of communities around the country understand what works (and at what cost) on their own problems. Meanwhile, the hope is that some new breakthroughs— be it bacteria or magic sand or something beyond our ken right now—will emerge in the new century and render much of this clunky, expensive hardware obsolete.

Cape Cod has become a technical classroom, of sorts. But the Cape's unusual relationship to the base is a lesson in something else as well: the military has never invited civilians who live around its bases to take part in real discussions about what will happen at those facilities. A remarkable range of community activists, with a remarkable range of styles and perspectives, found a way to insert themselves into that dialogue.

The experience could constitute a course in and of itself. But to understand how unusual and difficult an accomplishment this has been, it is important first to get a glimpse of what these "civilians" were up against:

There is a philosophy in the armed services, a mentality which can become a barrier because it was constructed to better the chances of survival in wartime, not to promote a partnership in peace. Historically, it would be fair to say that the military mindset has never championed flexibility, or openness.

And in a situation like this, that can become a big problem.

9

THE MILITARY MINDSET

Dan Santos, who is in a position to know, describes it like this:

"'You stay out.' That was the military attitude." Dan Santos served as an officer in the Navy for 12 years, left to start his own construction company in Rhode Island which ran smack into the hard times of the recession in the 1980s, and was hired to open the local office of the Installation Restoration Program in 1990. He stuck with the job until August, 1994; shortly after the Defense Department committed to funding the major work to contain the plumes, he took off for the private sector.

Over the course of more than four years, Santos spent a lot of time straddling fences:

He was a civilian employee on a military base. He worked for the federal government within a state bureaucracy; he tightroped not only between those two chains of command, but also among the various military personas. The Army National Guard, the Air National Guard, the Coast Guard, all had a say (or at least thought they had a say) in what he did. Federal bureaucrats at Andrews Air Force Base outside Washington, and the Adjutant General for the State of Massachusetts in Reading, both figured they should be calling the shots.

Meanwhile, he wasn't in a position to be left alone. Not only was the work high-profile, but Santos was running the only expanding operation in sight: he started with a desk and a pad of paper in 1990, and by 1994 was boss to 14 people with a $30 million budget. Those numbers are expected to do nothing but grow, while all other military budgets do little but shrink.

What made Dan Santos' position both interesting and important is that jobs like his will be more common in the years ahead. Civilians overseeing environmental cleanups will have to find ways to keep military brass and community activists working together. And, as Santos found, the military mindset is not an easy one to move in this direction:

"The key word in all of this is 'control,'" he says. "Ernie Keating wants control over what goes on on this base. And he doesn't have control over this process."

Ernest Keating, now a retired colonel, appointed in 1994 to head the "Unified Environmental Planning Function" office at the base, spent more than half of his 40 years in the National Guard serving at Camp Edwards. From the late 1970s into the early 1990s he took on various management titles: installation commander, deputy commander for support, support group commander.

"I'm referred to as the mayor out here," he smiles. "It's like running a little town. We have our police station, fire station, etcetera."

Keating omits a crucial distinction between this town and all others: as "mayor" here, he never had to stand for election. He was always appointed by his higher-ups.

"He comes from a military mentality," says Susan Walker from Sandwich. "He's top-down, keep the lid on. He has no understanding of grassroots participation."

"Ernie was head of the facility, the site commander, for 10 or 12 years," says Joel Feigenbaum. "He was there when some of the worst stuff was going on with the Fire Training Area, for instance. . . To make Ernie the guarantor of environmentalism on the base is ridiculous. If you have someone raping you, you don't rely on them for rape counseling."

Others agree with Santos that the real issue, from the military viewpoint, has to do with keeping control of the base on the base.

"The tactic is divide and conquer, and intimidation," says Susan Nickerson, executive director of the Association for the Preservation of Cape Cod (APCC). "He (Keating) has tried to intimidate APCC by writing directly to my president, and bypassing me. Brigadier General John Carlson (who Keating replaced), and Keating both were trying to incite discord between my board and me. . . It's something people working on their bases around the country should be aware of. It has to do with psychological overpowering of the citizenry. It happens through intimidation, fragmentation, and harassing certain people in the community. I think there's a 'military think,' that this is how you deal with the outside."

For Ernie Keating, the perspective is different: "Reflecting back on it," he says, "the community came out quite strong, in a demand tone. The military, from old habits, said, 'We're in a bureaucracy, we're not sure we have liability.' There was difficult communication. It was strained. And mixed in were some people with hidden agendas. They wanted to promote tension among people with good causes."

Maryanne Waygan, a registered nurse from Falmouth who tried to become involved in base issues around the time she learned she had breast cancer, saw a different situation than the one described by Keating:

"It was about five years ago now, I'd go to meetings. There was a lot of public interest. The agenda was set up—very structured, videos, slides, overheads. The presenters were in official uniforms with buttons and medals. They were telling people, not listening to people, and leaving no time for the general public to ask questions. It would be, 'Oh, got to get out of here, library's closing at 9 o'clock.' It was very exasperating. I mean, we really didn't need to know about the medals they won. . . And often, there was someone in the audience, anonymously, who was from the military. It was very intimidating."

Even the language used seemed to create barriers rather than open up lines of communication. There was an acronymn for everything, a veritable alphabet soup of terms which took weeks to digest, a language peculiar to the base and its environmental problems. It was entirely possible to hear officials in public meetings wonder whether CERCLA and RACER were covered re the CTU, whether MCLs might be exceeded in FS-1 as well as LF-1 and CS-10 (you know, BOMARC), whether HAZWRAP (a DOE contractor using ABB which formerly was ECJ) knew the ppb's for BTEX and EDB in FS-12, whether the NGB had talked with the EPA re USGS findings on VOCs like PCE or DCE, whether ANG and ARNG agreed with DEP and IRP about ATSDR's protocol re followup of BU's study. And the PAT needed answers so the SMB could talk at the TEAC about OpTech's PRP which needed to leave MMR in time for DoD to decide before UCCC and APCC (no longer in ABC without a TAG) protested the delay.

There were those who understood the lingo, and those who did not. It took a real commitment to learn it; people who had not or could not make that commitment often felt at sea as the discussions unfolded. This was not always an intentional result, but the use of this kind of jargon in any situation reflects an insider/outsider mentality. Lawyers, doctors, engineers, all employ their own versions. Its use does more than speed communication among those in the know; it excludes the rest.

In retrospect, and in short, there was a pervasive, stubborn resistance to opening up, to involving the community in the military's activities. People in the armed services follow orders; they don't interrogate superiors, and they often expect the same from the public. Suddenly, lay people who were supposed to be grateful for the protection they were receiving, and for the money base personnel spent in town, were asking questions and even angrily demanding answers.

What did this mean? It could only mean that these outside agitators were unpatriotic subversives.

"For career military people, as most of us are, it's that gung-ho, all-for-the-corps thing," muses Colonel Don Quenneville, Air Commander at Otis. "In our minds it was unconscionable for a citizen of our country to stand in the way of the defense of our nation."

According to Dan Santos, there were times inside the base, when everyone thought they were among like-minded friends, that a term for the activist public was used: "The Enemy."

Even within the base there was conflict about control, and chains of command. Santos had taken the position that he was a civilian, federal employee, working on the Air Guard's Installation Restoration Program, which meant that his boss was Ron Watson, who was in charge of those programs nationwide and worked in Washington DC. This did not sit well with the state military brass, which led to a remarkable confrontation:

Several years ago, Santos remembers, he was serving his weekend National Guard duty, which temporarily put him directly under the command of the state military hierarchy. Santos recalls being ordered into an office to meet with then-Adjutant General Wayne Wagner, and Brigadier General John Carlson (who was in charge of the environmental coordinating office at that time).

"It was a four-hour interrogation," he says. "I had to yes sir and no sir them, but inside I was laughing. They wanted to know my chain of command.

I got up, went to the blackboard, and drew a line from me to Ron Watson. Where were they? Where was the state? That's what they wanted to know. They were telling me I'm not a team player.

"Here I have two generals in my face, with the stars on the lapels and everything, and I'm thinking, 'They're afraid of me. They have no control over me.'"

General Carlson, meanwhile, became a symbol of what people saw as a military insensitivity which reached into intimidation.

In early 1993, responding to a request for information from Richard Hugus in Falmouth, Carlson added a note wishing Hugus "belated Happy Birthday wishes." Hugus had not told Carlson his birth date. The implication, as Sue Nickerson remembers, was clear: "We have a file on you."

"That's exactly how I took it," says Hugus. "Carlson wanted to show me he'd seen my file. How else would he know my birthday? He was showing me he had an intelligence thing behind him. It was designed to intimidate, but things like that just make people madder at them."

And when Joel Feigenbaum published his analysis of cancer rates in 1993, Carlson decided to write a letter to the editor in local papers which assailed Feigenbaum's numbers, and integrity:

"Fire up the Bunsen burner," wrote Carlson. "Professor Feigenbaum is cooking numbers again." Carlson argued that small raw figures could be made to look like large percentages, and that Feigenbaum's chronology of base activity was faulty as well. "What was that again?" Carlson concluded. "'There are lies, damn lies, and statistics.'"

People had plenty of disputes with Joel Feigenbaum, but to imply that elevated cancer rates on the Upper Cape were a fiction struck many as callous in the extreme. Among the many was the new Adjutant General, Raymond Vezina.

"(I)t is unfortunate that my first contact with the residents of Cape Cod is to state an apology," Vezina announced. He termed Carlson's letter an "unauthorized and unwarranted attack on Mr. Feigenbaum's personal and professional reputation." Barely a week later, it was announced that Carlson would "retire." The timing, Carlson insisted, was coincidence.

"It was an opportune time to make a change," General Vezina now says. He implies that it was Carlson's public attack, rather than his personal opinion, which Vezina couldn't condone.

Unfortunately, Retired General Carlson's perspective on the situation could not be included. He did not respond to repeated requests, made through Massachusetts Army National Guard headquarters, for an interview.

Vezina replaced Carlson with Ernie Keating, and has made it clear that issues of control, and chain of command, are still on the table:

"There has been a stovepipe approach, direct from the IRP (in Washington) to the base. My thought is that the unified environmental office (which Keating presently runs) will be the office that pretty much is the channel for all environmental activities on the Reservation. I've been making that very clear."

Yet even one of the most moderate public officials to work on the cleanup, Bourne Selectman Haydon Coggeshall, worries about the Adjutant General's interest in controlling this process:

"Given the person in that position, that's not a good idea," says Coggeshall. "Mr. Keating would represent a step backwards. Just as General Carlson represented the old style of military thinking, I'm not so sure Ernie isn't the same, but with a smile on his face. The attitude is that the public shouldn't be involved; give me some guys with stars and bars, and we'll get it done. But to shut the public out is ludicrous."

"Ultimately, I'm the guy they (the federal officials in charge of cleanup) have to answer to down there (at the base)," Vezina counters. "I'm the senior military guy in the state. . . Ernie, like everybody else, has learned some things. He's in tune with my philosophy: do what's best for the people on the Cape."

"I accept the commitment that we have to go back and clean up the mess that everybody's had a hand in," says Keating. "But you waste a lot of energy focusing on the past."

He lays responsibility on people outside of the military for much of the adversarial feelings which emerged: "Some people said, 'Who did it? Who's going to get blamed?' Another faction said, 'Let's go get'em! They're the bad guys!' That created a bad atmosphere. People took an insecure position, and lost focus on the goal of fixing the environment.

"We learned openness is necessary," Keating insists. "The truth is necessary. Get it out on the table. And then along comes a willingness to share resources. And what are we sharing? This base. The smartest thing we can do is put something in this base that the community can be excited about. . . (And so) it's a learning process, not to be offended when people talk angrily about your property."

Ernie Keating's choice of terms—referring to the base in a possessive way as his property—reveals the historic thinking of the military in general. It was exactly this attitude that confounded people through the 1980s.

"It was very paternalistic," says Susan Walker. "They were going to take care of everything. We should just relax and go away. . . We were seen as an annoyance."

Sue Nickerson from APCC says that one example of this attitude can be found in the way the military handled cleanup plans for the huge landfill area. Although "CERCLA" is supposed to guarantee public input and discussion about the future of Superfund sites, in this case the military basically decided to cap the landfill (and not actually clean out the pollution), spent millions of dollars in engineering work with that goal in mind, and only after all this investment yielded a specific plan was the public allowed to comment. In such a scenario, Nickerson charges, the public is little more than "window dressing."

Susan Walker remembers that Dan Santos tried to turn that attitude around in public meetings. "Dan would always say, 'It's the public's base, it's the public's money,'" she remembers. "And now, thank God, you can question the National Guard and no one will demean your patriotism. We've moved beyond that."

Santos is not sure the attitude actually has changed all that much: "John Carlson would come right out and say, 'They're my enemy.' But Ernie Keating won't. He'll say they're great, and all that. But it's all patronizing."

Even as a public meeting was announced to tell the public about the treatment plan approved for funding, Santos says that Keating was trying to step into the process. "He insisted we have one presenter, not a panel," Santos remembers. "He didn't want Joel (Feigenbaum) to speak. It was all about control. He was saying, 'This can't happen, it's not too late to change it.' We're throwing him a bone constantly. He has to have control."

Over the course of four years at the base, Santos went through an evolution in his approach. He started the job assuming that the mechanical side of cleanup was the most important piece of his work. Slowly, he was forced to the realization that communication with the public was even more crucial.

"In meetings, Dan would say, 'I'm going to tell you everything I know and it'll be the truth,'" remembers Susan Walker from Sandwich. "He had to say that about 50 times."

Looking back on it, Santos seems to feel that he spent years between rocks and hard places. His boss at the IRP office in Washington, Ron Watson, had taken a strong interest in Cape Cod's problems (which had the advantage of allowing Santos to cut through red tape and get programs moving). But Watson had very specific ideas about what should and shouldn't happen. Many times in public meetings, Watson made his positions clear: the Ashumet Valley plume should be allowed to go to the sea, unstopped and untreated. The FS-12 plume was outside base boundaries, and not his office's responsibility. The public should not be allowed into crucial meetings to discuss technical issues about cleanup.

This was the boss talking. In public, at least, Santos backed him up.

"In the past I've represented positions I don't believe in," Santos admits. "I won't do that anymore."

"Dan was very guarded, toeing the military line for a long time," says Sue Nickerson. "But he became educated to the need for public involvement. My perspective is that Dan began to fight with Ron, that there should be a new way. Dan was constantly in conflict. We (the community) were pressing him to do more and more, but Ron kept saying 'No.'"

Al Orlando, who serves as a Mashpee Water Commissioner and lives in the Briarwood neighborhood directly over one of the plumes, remembers that it took "five years of negotiating" before Watson and the rest of the federal bureaucracy would agree to help bring public water into the area in 1991. The state Department of Environmental Protection had been paying to bring bottled water to residents for years. The Mashpee Board of Health had declared the area contaminated and placed a moratorium on new building. "They (the feds) didn't respond very well at all," he says. "It shouldn't take five years to get a settlement."

Orlando remembers that Watson resisted paying for water hookups, or for a municipal system to replace private wells. "He would say, 'We don't want another $200 hammer,'" Orlando says. "Meanwhile, they had spent $15 to $20 million up to that time just for testing around the base. For $2 million, they could have taken care of everything in Briarwood."

It took years of effort, and intervention from Congressman Gerry Studds' office, to get an agreement. Even so, the military insisted on dividing the Briarwood community in two. East Briarwood was considered polluted, and homeowners received $1000 to pay for water hookups. West Briarwood was deemed only "half contaminated," and homeowners received $500.

"West Briarwood is now contaminated," Orlando believes. He feels that residents should be reimbursed the additional $500. "And now we have the same problem all over again. They never want to admit anything or pay for anything."

Many of the positions Ron Watson represented eventually were reversed: the Ashumet Valley plume of solvents will be treated. FS-12 is the responsibility of the base. Technical meetings have been opened to the public. Briarwood in particular and Mashpee in general have gotten a great deal of financial assistance. That seems to indicate that Dan Santos was lobbying inside the process for the kind of change that activists were pressing for on the outside. Or, as Richard Hugus believes, Santos was forced into the changes along with all the others.

"He's not as offensive as some of the older folks, who were too rigid to bend," says Richard Hugus. "But I don't think I'll ever trust Dan Santos. I've seen him prevaricate too many times."

Hugus believes that Dan Santos represented a new approach on the surface only, a more sophisticated management style for the military nationwide which was adopted from the various "inclusive" corporate role models taught at business school. Hugus wrote "A Bureaucrat's Guide to Avoiding Direct Answers to Questions from the Public" as a kind of tongue-in-cheek ode to what he sees as the new tactic. Some of his points were:

"1. If confronted with an inconvenient question at a public meeting, praise the questioner for his/her contribution and, with apologies, defer it to a later item on the agenda. . .

"2. If confronted by a group of people with chronic annoying questions, invite members of the group to form a study committee. . .

"5. Give the public the impression that they are involved in 'the decision-making process.' Then, should things go wrong, the public can be blamed for the failure. . .

"9. If all else fails, answer the annoying questioner by saying you just don't know. Show your sincerity by referring the question to someone not present who does know. Then the issue is between the annoying questioner and some individual who may or may not answer. In any case a public airing will be avoided."

All of this assumes, of course, that good faith is not at the heart of these discussions, that anyone representing the military side can only be another expression of the same mentality. Dan Santos realizes that a fundamental suspicion, particularly among people who remember the Vietnam War, can paint everyone with the same broad brush:

"It's very difficult to represent the military, and the federal government," he says. "There's a great deal of mistrust. Right there, that's two strikes against me, and if I screw up, there's three strikes and I'm out." Despite this, many came to trust Dan Santos, and to see him as a key reason why there has finally been forward movement to clean up the base. "I can't say enough good things about him," says Falmouth Selectman Virginia Valiela.

"Over time, I developed a great deal of respect for Dan Santos," says Susan Walker. "That's understanding he doesn't run the Pentagon, and doesn't always get his way."

"I think he's done a helluva good job, no question," says Mark Forest, head of Congressman Studds' Cape Cod office.

"The point here is that the military is not monolithic," says Sue Nickerson. "And I believe that is true all over the country. As activist groups begin to work on their problems, they need to find out who their friends are, who's sympathetic."

What is important is not the personalities. It is the perspectives which the personalities embody. From time to time, and base to base, the names will be entirely different but the perspectives might not change at all. On Cape Cod, the base has been pried open enough so that the public has gotten a glimpse of how the military hierarchy works, about the importance of control and the discomfort of having to involve "outsiders." When structure, rules, and chain of command give way to the messier, less predictable, more open democratic process, some people are threatened.

But what is also important is that not everyone responds the same way. To assume that every person in the armed service, or public service, is there for the same reasons with the same attitude is not much different than any kind of stereotyping— including the kind that some base personnel apparently have applied to citizens who dare question them. It makes life simpler. It offers the luxury of dismissing individuals and their nuances. But it also denies the opportunity for a new consensus, for unexpected allies, for deep change.

"If people in the community weren't willing to trust me, my job would have been a lot harder," says Dan Santos. After four and a half years working on the base, he is ready to step back into the private sector. "I'm tired of getting beat up," he says, but he cannot offer any optimism that this long process has taught the military's powers-that-be the value of open decision-making and public participation:

"They're only doing this (community involvement) to keep people quiet," Santos concludes. "Keep them quiet. And until that attitude changes, we're in trouble. Because it's not about keeping people quiet. It's about keeping people involved."

10

ACTIVISM, TACTICS AND TENSIONS

If there are different shades of thinking within the military about how to involve civilians in environmental decision making, then there is a double rainbow of opinion among those civilians about what tactics work best.

For some, Malcolm X's famous quote seems to be the relevant guiding philosophy: "By any means necessary."

For some, "working within the system" has meant avoiding threats, eschewing lawsuits, assuming good faith, and in many ways hoping for the best.

Some people in this long process have seen themselves as catalysts, others as consensus builders. Stubborn resolve and emotional barrage have both played their parts. There have been political decisions and disagreements at many junctures: about how best to create progress, about how best to open the closed doors at the base, about whom to trust, about short-term goals.

All of this sounds familiar to people who have been involved in any kind of grassroots effort. Vietnam War protests, civil rights organizing, election campaigns, neighborhood coalitions to preserve open space, all eventually grapple with the fundamental question of what really makes for change, and what is the real definition of success. This sloppy, imperfect, galling, frustrating, never ending process, this stew of people and ideas and tactics, is the messy stuff behind that dry, smooth cliche to which we are all supposed to aspire, that popular notion referred to as "public participation." In the body politic, this is the guts of it, the guts of democracy.

One of the old saws says that legislation is like sausage: it's not a good idea to look too closely at how either of them is made, because you'll lose your appetite for both. Public involvement is something like that, too, because the truth of it is never neat or clean. The goal might be virtually holy, but in the meantime, well, it's just a bunch of people trying to muddle along as best they can. It ain't always pretty, but it's always essential.

As far as pollution at Cape Cod's military base is concerned, we now have the luxury of more than a decade of hindsight. What's more, we have arrived at a fulcrum moment. All the pushing and pulling, the cajoling and confronting, has resulted in a Defense Department commitment to spend several hundred million dollars to stop these plumes. That in itself is a remarkable victory on the federal playing field. It suggests that something right (albeit something slow) has happened so far; it also suggests that much more of the same will be needed in the next phase, when massive amounts of money and effort finally translate into massive amounts of treatment.

A casual observer would expect to find a coalition of people from the towns surrounding the military base working in concert to stop the pollution. In fact, such a coalition has never really existed. The base has become a common concern (some would say a common enemy) for people who otherwise would have very little to do with each other, whose ideas about life (let alone problem solving) vary profoundly, who see literally everything from different perspectives.

It may sound Pollyanna-ish, and some of the people involved will not agree, but luxurious hindsight seems to suggest something else: every sincere person has found a way to contribute to the progress so far, just as every sincere person has at times slowed it down. The picture that emerges is a mosaic, a jigsaw puzzle of tactics and attitudes, carrots and sticks, good cops and bad. Some call this "grassroots," and in terms of describing change that is appropriate: for a long time, it seems like nothing is happening, and then, somehow, small roots crack concrete.

For Joel Feigenbaum, push usually has to come to shove to make things move in a situation like this. In essence, Joel has applied labor organizing tactics to the Massachusetts Military Reservation. His roots are in the Eugene

McCarthy for President, Vietnam War protest campaigns of the 1960s, followed by years of community organizing in Lynn, Massachusetts. He makes his money as a college mathematics professor, but clearly his passion has become his fight against the military's local presence.

Since the early 1980s, when he first became involved, his son has died in a tragic accident; he looks at this work as "a memorial to him." He and his wife (who joined him in the early years of activism) are now divorced. Yet Joel remains. To him, there is a direct continuity from where he was, and why he first got involved in organizing, to where he is today:

"A lot of this contamination is a direct result of Vietnam-support activities," says Feigenbaum. "It's so ironic. Vietnam was really the first case of true toxic warfare, aimed at vegetation. And then the legacy is a despoiling of the land here at one of the most prized human habitats in the country. It's a burning irony." It is important, he argues, to "view the National Guard as a corporate entity, responsible beyond the individual personas." Therefore, even people like Dan Santos, who appeared to be committed to progress, are not necessarily to be trusted; at various times Joel referred to him as "a double agent," one of many "fascists" or "Nazis," as the Guard Bureau's "boy." He will see "the military's tentacles" running through the community via "the Chamber of Commerce. It's not just that the boys drink in the bars. People provide all sorts of things to that base. It's a city out there." And, he assumes, people are reluctant to bite the hand that feeds.

For Falmouth Selectman Virginia Valiela, the journey has been just as long as Joel's, but the road passed through a different landscape. It was the first Earth Day in 1970, not the Vietnam War, which was the genesis of her local political involvement. She had moved to Falmouth six months earlier, and ran a unique event for the time: a drive to recycle paper. A town recycling committee grew out of that first effort, and Virginia was drawn into local politics, first as a commissioner for the Falmouth Department of Public Works and then as a selectman. A young mother with two children had become a politician.

She knew about the Ashumet Valley plume, and the base sewage treatment plant. She kept one of the mysterious, blackened rocks from the edge of Ashumet Pond on her kitchen window sill as a reminder. But politically, and temperamentally, she did not prize confrontation.

"There seemed to be three ways to solve this," to make the military take responsibility for the contamination, she explains. "A technical, legal, or political solution. We decided to set up a dialogue, to try a technical approach... From 1981 through 1985, that was our tack. It was very slow, and very discouraging. But it did make progress."

Meanwhile, Susan Walker, a school teacher from Sandwich who would later represent her town on the Barnstable County Assembly of Delegates, wanted the military to put a fence around the base so children in the neighborhood wouldn't stumble on yet more unexploded ordnance as they explored the woods. Her choice of tactic was clear: "Political pressure," she says. Her background was in the nuclear freeze movement; when she came to find out that the Impact Area (virtually in her backyard) was being used to test components of the MX missile, her interest in the base deepened.

"It was a small group, not well organized," Susan remembers. The Feigenbaums were instrumental, along with Stephanie Adams, a psychologist then living in Falmouth, and her husband Duke Ellis. The group took a name: Upper Cape Concerned Citizens, UCCC.

"For many years," remembers Stephanie, "elected people, business people, real estate people, really didn't want any (bad) publicity. There was no support for concern about the base. Nobody wanted to talk about this. It was worse than pulling teeth. People actually tried to discourage us, and discredit us."

Another social factor at work was the strong presence of retired military personnel in the towns surrounding the base. Bourne in particular had the reputation as almost a "company town," because so many past and present servicemen lived there. Many took criticism of the base personally. Richard Kolbert, a flight engineer at Otis for more than 10 years, expressed what at the time was far too common a sentiment: "I think this Feigenbaum should be put up against a wall and shot. A tree hugger is fine, but there's extremes to it."

For years, the Feigenbaums bore the brunt of anger aimed at local activists. Joel Feigenbaum remembers hate calls, anti-Semitic epithets, threats along the lines of, "You better watch out when you start your car in the morning." When Freddie Feigenbaum rose at a Sandwich Town Meeting to urge a moratorium on certain activities on the base, boos and hisses would cascade. There was Red-baiting similar to the sorts of things said during the early 1960s about the scientists opposed to a "nuclear park" for Otis. The group's acronym was given a new, sarcastic meaning; UCCC came to be "Upper Cape Concerned Communists."

"At any point in time, there were about 20 people," remembers Stephanie Adams. "Six or eight really were doing the work. With Joel, people would come and go—he's not an easy person to work with. . . But the whole thing was his initiative. He has a deep passion about the issue. He was the mover."

Through the mid-1980s, there were some successes, and some surprises. Fences eventually were installed around the base perimeter—only after help and intervention from US Congressman Gerry Studds. Demonstrations at the gates led to arrests, a trial, and publicity. High cancer rates were revealed, forcing public health studies. Throughout, Joel Feigenbaum staked out the most confrontive positions. He used the press and the courts to publicize two of his beliefs which intersected on base property: that US military activity in Central America was immoral (including National Guardsmen being sent to Honduras), and that the base was poisoning its neighbors.

"Joel's second major impact," remembers Susan Walker, "was that he read the technical material put out by the IRP office on the base. They knew they were being watched. He was informed. The military had to do things in a more timely fashion, and be more honest about the problems. I was in awe of what Joel knew. He would nail them time after time."

Meanwhile, Virginia Valiela was plugging along, meeting by meeting. Engineers tried to get Falmouth's public supply well back in action by pumping less, hoping the pollution deep underground wouldn't be sucked into the pipe. The experiment failed. By 1985, private wells in Ashumet Valley were proven contaminated.

"We could have sued," she says. "But we still had a feeling that wouldn't solve the problem." Finally, in June of 1986, the National Guard agreed to pay Falmouth nearly $4 million to replace the well, and install town water in certain areas.

Valiela remembers that some tentative attempts to hold open meetings between the military brass and Cape residents began around this time. The state had a new adjutant general, Anthony Spadorcia. "I remember Joel and his wife Freddie turned up at some of these meetings," Virginia notes, "and they were very angry with this man. The thing began to escalate. I saw an opportunity for dialogue falling apart. One day, Joel showed up with a television camera. Spadorcia got up and left, and the door closed. That was the end of our opportunity."

Dr. Feigenbaum would argue that access and participation were crucial, that the military had no right to define the terms; nothing had been lost. When the Otis Task Force, an advisory group whose members are appointed by the governor, held open meetings, Joel would try to introduce his own agenda and questions, much to the chagrin of the chairman of the group, then-Bourne Selectman Marie Oliva.

"She told me if I said the word 'cancer' one more time, she'd have me thrown out," Feigenbaum remembers. "I stood up, said 'cancer,' and she had me physically removed."

"It's no different than town meeting," says Marie Oliva. "Joel Feigenbaum or anybody, it doesn't matter. You have to have meetings conducted in an orderly fashion, or you have chaos. . . Some of the tactics didn't serve any real purpose except for media attention and confrontation."

"That meeting was not in any way chaotic," remembers Stephanie Adams. "They didn't want people to speak for more than three minutes at a time, and Joel had all kinds of things he wanted to cover. It was ludicrous. . . They had no information. No questions were answered. And the more pointed the questions, the more they baited Joel."

Given Virginia Valiela's approach, it is not surprising that she sees this sort of situation in different terms:

"The problem with being too emotional is that you jam the circuits of the people who you need to make the change," she says. "There's a lot of unjamming that needs to get done."

"Nothing that anybody does will ever entirely satisfy Joel," says Mark Forest, head of Congressman Gerry Studds' Cape Cod office. "But he's pushing for the right things."

That constant push—aggressive, in-your-face, irritating—was alienating, but it served a greater purpose; Joel widened the frame of reference a great deal. He was the radical, unpredictable, antagonistic force, an intellectual 800-pound gorilla. Anyone more moderate than him was much more attractive for base personnel to deal with. There was nothing premeditated about this, nothing planned and executed, but there were times when the "good activists," as Feigenbaum disparagingly puts it, seemed to have more clout because their alternative was clear and present.

"The good cop/bad cop thing can be an effective organizing tool," acknowledges Susan Walker.

This unwitting strategy became more pronounced in the late 1980s and early 1990s, when a new generation of activists arrived on the scene.

On the one hand, Richard Hugus from Falmouth began providing support for Feigenbaum's position, as well as some of his tactics. "I took the typical radical stance," Richard remembers. "Don't work within the system, but change the whole system. This is a federal institution that is indifferent to local people. That's why the pollution happened, and that's why the cleanup has been so slow." Hugus spun off his own group, which he called the Otis Conversion Project. The message was clear: not only should the plumes be cleaned up, but the military base should be shut down and converted for civilian uses.

In Mashpee, James Kinney had educated himself about the plumes, and was amazed that town officials were so nonchalant in the face of such danger. He began to push Mashpee selectmen, arriving at a meeting with fish caught in Johns Pond and asking, "Would you eat them, when we don't know for sure if the pond is safe? Would you let your kids swim in this pond?" He felt resistance not only from the military, but the local boards and state officials as well. "They should all be called the Departments of Public Reassurance," he says. "Their job is to minimize, minimize, minimize."

Meanwhile, Susan Nickerson, executive director of the Association for the Preservation of Cape Cod, had decided to urge her board of directors to commit a good deal of the organization's energy to working on military base issues. Prior to 1990, APCC had been enmeshed in the political fight to create a regulatory body now known as the Cape Cod Commission. The base became a logical next step for a Cape Cod environmental group; clearly, it was the biggest pollution threat on the peninsula.

"I see our position as being a recognized environmental group with some degree of clout," Nickerson explains. "We have older, retired people among our 3000 to 4000 members. We have some money. I think people at the base thought we were legitimate, because of our history, the things we were involved in, and the way we operate: open lines of communication, talk to everybody, and don't be extreme in our approach. Don't shout insults at public meetings, or take part in civil disobedience."

It had taken most of the decade, but the community activists were finally being considered legitimate even among people in the community who were Red-baiting them years earlier. When the base was placed on the Superfund's National Priority List in 1989, the federal government essentially admitted that the "agitators" had been right all along. Support for their activities widened, and deepened.

By 1990, these community groups had organized themselves into a coalition which they called the Alliance for Base Cleanup, ABC. Joel Feigenbaum's group (Upper Cape Concerned Citizens), Susan Walker's group (Responsible Environmental Protection for Sandwich), the Ashumet Valley Property Owners, Inc., and Susan Nickerson's APCC joined to apply for funding from the US Environmental Protection Agency. With the Superfund designation came an opportunity for a technical assistance grant. The idea was to hire independent experts to analyze the scientific reports created by the military's consultants, assess their quality and meaning, and translate them into understandable English.

The original ABC was a short-lived phenomenon, dissolving little more than a year after its creation. Susan Walker's group was the first to break out of the coalition.

"One of our members was being browbeaten during the meetings," Walker remembers. "There was not respect for different points of view. People were demeaned and ridiculed. This happened to a REPS member in her seventies... The process was painful, and unrespectful."

After much soul searching, Sue Nickerson urged APCC's board of directors to pull out as well. From her point of view, there had been an attempt to strong-arm her organization, to force it into positions her board did not want to take.

"We tried very hard," she says. "But there was too much unwillingness to work cooperatively. It was their way, or no way. From my point of view, Joel Feigenbaum wanted to run APCC and I couldn't tolerate that." She came to see his tactics as a form of intellectual bullying; he would never agree to disagree, never compromise.

"APCC is always ready to play the role of 'the good activists,' the reasonable ones, as opposed to 'those bad guys,'" says Feigenbaum. "Non-profits seek support from a variety of conservative sources, like banks even. I'm not beholden to anybody. I do my analysis and I lay it out. That translates into 'personality issues.' But to put the personality issue first, that's silly."

Joel says he wanted the group to negotiate from a tougher stance, to hold out for more money, to push harder, to make sure resources to look at all the plumes were included. He believes the reason APCC pulled out of the coalition was because military personnel, particularly Ernie Keating, were very upset over a dramatic leaflet written by Jamie Kinney which urged people to come to a public meeting by asking the question, "Is Otis Killing You?"

Susan Walker, who joined APCC's board of directors four years later, remembers it differently. "Joel has no respect for different strategies or tactics," she says. "To Joel, the end is the only thing you think about. To me, coming from the peace community, the process is important too. You don't demean people."

"Joel has a vision, but he's not great at having other people assist at that level," says Stephanie Adams. "He's not good at maintaining alliances. If there wasn't someone else there to do that, it didn't happen."

Feigenbaum believes that all this discussion about his "personality" shouldn't even be a part of a book of this kind. He senses cultural issues and political undercurrents in the context of this kind of talk. He also feels that focusing on such things is a tactic widely used to discredit activists.

"They'll use the term about outspoken people," he says, "that they're 'impolite.' Look, I know how to be courteous, I'm a full professor at a community college. . . The 'personality issue' is a dodge for pusillanimity," he concludes, "and that means lack of courage."

For Richard Hugus, the collapse of ABC meant something else entirely: "That was the last time I thought we could work within the system in any way," he concludes.

Nickerson was interested in working deeper into "the system." "I think I was able to use APCC to my advantage, to have access to people," she says. "I don't want that to sound too manipulative, but I was invited to meetings, or had discussions with various people, who would exclude Joel because they couldn't cope with him. This also had its down side: I felt APCC was being played off these other people. So it was a difficult row to hoe."

Access to the Technical Environmental Affairs Committee, known as the TEAC, a crucial forum created by the military's IRP office to explore all key issues related to pollution on base, became the dilemma's symbol. The meetings were closed, open only to those people who the military decided had information to give, and a direct stake in the situation. Joel Feigenbaum, despite his years of activism, was excluded. The Ashumet Valley Property Owners were included, because their property was affected—and because they were less confrontational. Virginia Valiela, as a Falmouth selectman, was included. And Sue Nickerson, after months of discussion, was invited to attend.

There was a tactical decision to be made: should she keep solidarity and stay out until the meetings were opened to everyone, or should she go in? She might not bring the same analytical judgment to the table that was Joel

Feigenbaum's trademark, but even so, would her presence, in her own way, keep the heat on?

She decided to go in.

"If Ron Watson makes a policy to keep us out of TEAC meetings, that's National Guard policy. Everybody understands that," argues Feigenbaum. "But if Nickerson accepts an invitation to go to these meetings and represents the community, that's the kind of co-optation that's really dangerous."

Not everyone agreed. "I thought it was a better idea to muscle your way in piece by piece," remembers Stephanie Adams.

It took several years before these TEAC meetings finally were opened to anyone who wanted to sit in. In the meantime, Nickerson continued to attend, to lobby for them to be open, and to provide detailed minutes of all discussions to anyone who wasn't allowed to participate. "It used to be that APCC was in the fold, and the others were out of the fold, and that was a difficult position," she now says. "But I did it because things were accomplished."

Denis LeBlanc watched this process from an interesting perspective. In the early years, base officials were suspicious of him because he was independent, and even angry at him because his work showed the magnitude of their problems. But over time, his scientific expertise came to be trusted. In some ways he was inside, in other ways outside.

"The Feigenbaums are there to keep the pressure on," he says. "Let's face it: without that heat, things would slow down. They serve a real purpose. I think their role is essential, and essentially positive—not that it's always pleasant to bear the brunt of it.

"And then," LeBlanc continues, "there are people who really are part of the solution, like Virginia, and Susan Nickerson." Their role, LeBlanc feels, is to negotiate, conciliate, build a workable consensus—not just pressure.

Given these distinctions, it is no surprise that the ABC coalition broke apart. But what might not have been anticipated is that even some of the most dedicated people in Feigenbaum's Upper Cape group fell away from him as well. Stephanie Adams, for instance, stopped her involvement. Partly she was worn down by years of volunteer work, and by deep distrust of the military. Partly her life and private practice needed more attention. But Joel Feigenbaum's tactics also took a toll on her.

"Joel's attacking Susan Nickerson really got me," says Adams. "And he'd attack other people too. When he was doing it with the military it wasn't as painful to me. But when he undermined any chances of keeping a coalition together, it was very painful. . . Breaking alliances with Susan didn't make any sense. She was such a useful part of the process."

The Ashumet Valley Property Owners, on their own now that the coalition was defunct, applied for a new technical assistance grant, and won $50,000 to hire their own experts "to be referees and interpreters," as Chris Dunn from the group puts it. Their work is limited to the Ashumet Valley plume, to Johns and Ashumet ponds. To this day, there has been no funding for basewide, independent scientific analysis.

And to this day, distrust among the various activists runs almost as deep as distrust of the military. "The Ashumet Valley Property Owners Association has been bought, in my opinion," says Jamie Kinney. Richard Hugus calls them "base friendly," which for him is far from a compliment.

"Our approach," says Chris Dunn, "is to say, 'We're here, they're there, we aren't going away and they aren't either. So let's get through this together.'... When this was getting off the ground, you needed a guy like Joel Feigenbaum, who was carrying the crusade and keeping the heat up. It's paid off. And they've found a way to get him involved. I was happy to see that."

This issue of involvement, trying to create a structure that would both include people and force results, fascinated George Crombie, who had stepped in as regional director of the Massachusetts Department of Environmental Protection in March of 1992. Crombie had come from a public works background, most recently attacking a pollution problem in Vermont. He had studied other Superfund sites around the country, trying to understand why so many of them had failed to get anything done, and he was convinced that community involvement was the key missing link. In this way, he was a welcome, positive change from previous bureaucrats in the state agency.

"My observations were that there was a tremendous amount of so-called 'studies' going on in this project, but it was very fragmented," Crombie remembers. "No one really focused on what we should accomplish, and what is the time line. . . And I discovered that many individuals on the local level wanted the same thing. But the bureaucracy—the EPA, the military—were off doing their thing. The locals really weren't part of the process."

When Crombie asked why the TEAC meetings weren't open, he was told that the people were "unruly," or that the public wouldn't understand "technical issues." He thought these were "poor excuses" that basically "allowed the military to control the process and the time lines."

Crombie, working with Jim Begley from his office, made it clear that the state environmental people could care less about the CERCLA process, or about all the other rules and regulations which seemed to be driving study after study after study. "We need a plan," he said. "We need a plan. Then we'll work through the other pieces."

The structure which Crombie advocated was a Senior Executive Board, made up of selectmen from the four local towns, the EPA, Crombie's DEP, the Adjutant General, and the head of the Air Force's IRP program. And then a series of "action teams," to get into the nitty gritty of specific issues and make recommendations to the executive board. Within these "teams," key players could sit down, face to face, and deal with the problems at hand. The barrier between "inside" and "outside" wouldn't disappear, but at least it would break down.

It took more than a year of discussion, but a framework along these lines was adopted. Crombie takes much of the credit: "The real structure and formulation came out of here," he says, meaning his office. Others, particularly Dan Santos, say that this approach was not Crombie's brainchild alone. Regardless, suddenly there was a mechanism, a way to deal with public policy issues that was more encompassing than military fiat.

The benefits of the new structure became apparent immediately: at the first meeting of the "plume process action team," there was strong support among the members (Joel Feigenbaum, Susan Nickerson, Jamie Kinney, and Denis LeBlanc included) to study all the plumes on the base, with the idea that a plan could be developed to treat them all simultaneously. Ron Watson, then head of the IRP, strongly opposed the idea; he wanted to move one plume at a time. The group took its recommendation to the newly-created Senior Management Board, which heard the arguments and sided with the overview approach; let's try to contain all the plumes at once. A crucial decision which would speed up the process in the coming months, and eventually create a strong plan for cleanup, had been reached because of open debate in a democratic structure.

"All along, the design was intended to get the military to give up the reins," says Crombie, "to force them in a subtle way to do that. We were successful."

People who had basically been on the sidelines for as long as 10 years suddenly were in the game. A slow but significant thaw in relations took place. Joel Feigenbaum joined the TEAC meetings—and the sky didn't fall in. As a member of the plume study team, he helped play an instrumental role in developing the containment plan that has been adopted. He joins National Guard personnel as well as less combative activists like Sue Nickerson in making public presentations about cleanup plans for the base. And his presence lends credibility among those people who have come to distrust the military.

For all the falling ins and falling outs, the mesh of characters who have remained active around base issues has created an unwitting synergy, a tactical fit which produces results. A good example of how this continues to work can be found by looking at one group set up by the military to explore a specific problem: the Ashumet and Johns Pond Task Force.

Pressure had been building since 1989 to focus attention on the two ponds at the southern boundary of the base for many reasons: people live around them, swim in them, fish in them. Meanwhile, the National Guard's own maps give the clear impression that both are receiving contamination from years of dumping in the industrial area of the base (including the runways themselves).

Jamie Kinney was banging fish on the table in front of the Mashpee selectman, urging studies. Chris Dunn and the Ashumet Valley association were lobbying for studies too, in a more genteel fashion. Virginia Valiela was pushing for the same thing. Dan Santos agreed, and wanted to use the opportunity to put to work some of the "inclusive" management techniques that he and George Crombie (among others) had been advocating. In his opinion, the Association for the Preservation of Cape Cod was the best group to pull the task force together, because it could assemble scientific support, it had broad community contacts, and Susan Nickerson had established credibility both inside and outside the base. Would APCC lead the task force? Nickerson and her board of directors agreed, with the understanding that the meetings would be open to the public—including Joel Feigenbaum.

The volunteer task force began its work in the fall of 1991, years before the phrase "process action team" was even considered. The group put together a study plan: the two ponds should be analyzed to see if the plumes are changing the water, affecting fish and plant life. They should be compared to other ponds in the region. Scientific protocols and research programs were created, but the bottom line questions were always blunt: Are these ponds safe to swim in? Are the fish from these ponds safe to eat?

By June, 1994, a phalanx of researchers (funded by the military's IRP office to support the task force) gathered to present a summary of findings from the first year of field work. Dr. Barbara Walton, a scientist working with

HAZWRAP out of a national lab in Oak Ridge, Tennessee, summarized two volumes of preliminary results.

Speaking very cautiously, saying that she was only a consultant, insisting that local boards of health should be the final arbiters, she indicated that work to date showed that the ponds looked to be in decent shape. Contaminants of various kinds had been detected in fish samples, but "not in amounts above what is generally deemed safe to eat." Mussels are one important indicator of an area's health, because they filter so much water and catch much of what is in the environment. The freshwater mussels, she reported, basically looked good. Some of the larger and older catfish and bass in the ponds showed tumors, lesions, and even some mercury contamination. This was troubling, but it was unclear whether it was unique to these ponds, common to all ponds in the region, or even whether these growths were a response to environmental pollution or not.

Various researchers involved in the project supported this assessment in various ways. Heads were nodding around the table; so far, so good, seemed to be the general consensus.

And then, almost as an afterthought, Dr. Walton mentioned that Joel Feigenbaum and Susan Nickerson had been interested in some information about one chemical apparently found in mussels sampled in the ponds. It is known by the tongue-twisting name N-nitrosodimethylamine, one of many chemicals in the nitrosamine family. She felt obliged, professionally speaking, to report back to them on this question:

This substance is extremely dangerous, she explained. Small amounts are lethal, or cause cancer. It breaks down quickly in sunlight, but it also shows up in cured food, and sometimes appears in the process that makes beer and whiskey. No more than one part per billion is allowed in the malt used for alcohol. The reason some people worry about hot dogs is because nitrosamines are found in them.

Why would a nitrosamine reportedly show up in freshwater mussels? It could be a natural process of the intestines. But then again, one chemical used in the production of liquid rocket fuel prior to 1976 so happened to create a nitrosamine byproduct. This type of fuel was used for the BOMARC missiles.

It took some time, it took some prodding, but eventually another fact emerged: according to the lab reports, this nitrosamine found in mussels collected from these two ponds tested as high as 600 parts per billion.

"600 parts per billion?" Joel Feigenbaum erupted. "These mussels are worse than hot dogs." He dove into available literature to prove his point: bacon, by way of comparison, ranges from one to 44 parts per billion.

Other researchers from Oak Ridge joined the discussion. First of all, they noted, no one from this area eats freshwater mussels. Yes, they did test mussels from other ponds—when they could find them, because not all ponds have mussels. True, the other test results showed nowhere near this amount of the nitrosamine; in fact, other mussels had virtually none. Yet mussels bought off the shelf at a market in Tennessee, a random comparison, showed even higher levels, double the amounts found in the pond's mussels.

Wait a second, Jamie Kinney said. "I've seen children collecting mussels from the pond. I know some people eat them."

Wait a second, said Joel Feigenbaum. "One sample from a market in Tennessee is your control? What kind of science is that?"

"We're in a situation," said Kinney, "where Exxon is cleaning up the coast. That's what we have here."

Wait a second, said Richard Hugus. Even now, after this work and these reassurances, "people don't have any idea what these plumes are doing to the ponds."

"That's absolutely correct," said Dr. John Stegeman, a researcher from Woods Hole whose own studies of the ponds suggested that the discharge from outboard motors might be doing more harm than anything else identified so far.

"See what I have to put up with?" stormed Feigenbaum, as the meeting broke up.

The science was not conclusive; more tests, more comparisons need to be done. Some people left the meeting feeling that a mountain had been made of a molehill; others felt that a danger signal had been buried in the data, and was revealed only after being dug up.

Regardless, within a week of the meeting, Susan Nickerson as chair of the task force had made sure that the boards of health of all four towns around the base, as well as the county, received a report of the information revealed. Findings about nitrosamines and mercury were detailed in a fact finding sheet printed on APCC stationery.

"According to information received by the Task Force," the statement read, "taking mussels from the pond for human consumption would appear to constitute a serious health risk." The statement did not recommend any specific action. It simply reported the information.

This certainly was not enough for Richard Hugus, who began his next publication of "MMR Watch," a newsletter about the base, with an article titled, "The Ashumet & Johns Pond Task Farce (sic)." The speculation about other causes of pollution in the ponds met with his disdain:

"But what about the plumes? Groundwater plumes caused by millions of gallons of dumped toxics at a nearby military base apparently cause no harm whatsoever. Thanks to the Ashumet/Johns Pond Task Force, we now know that motorboats and bacon are to blame!"

Does this small case study prove that science funded by the military is conducted in bad faith? Was this a form of coverup? Some would say yes; some would say no. The information was there, the data presented. Yet the emphasis and interpretation was very different than what some community leaders would apply.

Does this case study prove that informed oversight is essential for scientific effort like this? Absolutely.

There was another twist to this story that suggests this conclusion even more strongly: weeks after the presentation, HAZWRAP officials contacted the task force to announce that their science, apparently, was faulty. The chemical "was incorrectly reported as a positive-detect in mussels collected from Ashumet and Johns Ponds," according to a statement issued by the laboratory involved. All data evaluated would need to be re-examined to ensure against "false-positive results, false-negative results; and misidentified compounds."

And in the weeks that followed, independent analysts concluded that there was indeed a major error in the research. The chemical identified was not N-nitrosodimethylamine, but rather a common kind of fatty acid which is not hazardous to health.

In short, the alarm sounded was false, but it raised serious questions about all of the work done to date, and forced the scientists to analyze their material more carefully.

Meanwhile, this case study also shows how remarkably different approaches can dovetail into revelations, and action. Jamie Kinney and Chris Dunn, among others, pressured for the work. Sue Nickerson bridged between the base and the community to make the dialogue possible. Citizens charged the scientists with the responsibility of gathering the data. Joel Feigenbaum confronted the "experts," demanding more detail and another analysis. Sue Nickerson made sure that communication moved beyond the walls of the meeting room. Richard Hugus, still not satisfied, added a radical reinterpretation.

This kind of thing has been going on for years, issue after issue, meeting after meeting. An overwhelming persistence, a stubborn marathon of involvement, has brought about some unprecedented success, as we will see in the next chapter. It took the extraordinary combination of tactics, styles, and characters to move this cleanup forward. From community to community the names change, but probably the same range of motion and opinion would be needed to accomplish this task: the equivalent of pushing a big rock up a steep hill.

The lesson is that progress is possible. The daunting truth is that it takes ceaseless commitment to make it happen.

Meanwhile, a remarkable thing has happened: the mainstream caught up to Joel Feigenbaum's positions. Concern about cancer on Cape Cod is not some kind of fringe alarmism anymore. Demands that the military clean up the base, no matter what the cost, are not the stuff of some left-wing plot with a "hidden agenda." Once again, in a small way, the analogy is to bigger social issues like the civil rights movement and the Vietnam War: eventually, middle ground shifted, or was pushed, toward a place that at first had been considered radical or unpatriotic.

"A lot of folks on the Cape came to the same conclusion that the wild-eyed people came to," laughs Mark Forest.

And when consensus moves like that, when the League of Women Voters, the Barnstable County Assembly of Delegates, the Association for the Preservation of Cape Cod, and Joel Feigenbaum all find themselves on the same side of the issue, then change cannot be too far behind.

Yet if grassroots activism really has two goals—to make something better, and to organize and "empower" broad groups of people to make that improvement—then the work has only been half successful. For all the effort over all the years, it still seems that only a small cadre is involved in base issues. Many who were politicized years ago have dropped out, worn down by the long process, intimidated by resistance from within as well as by incendiary attitudes without. The "community" has not become "organized." Joel Feigenbaum's Upper Cape Concerned Citizens group is tiny. Richard Hugus' Otis Conversion Project is tiny. Jamie Kinney's Mashpee Alliance for Base Cleanup is tiny. The Association for the Preservation of Cape Cod has not expanded its membership in any dramatic way because of its base activism.

There doesn't seem to be any eagerness to join hands and leap into the next issue, to expand the vision of a solid coalition.

This was a moment, if ever there was one, for people to find common ground and unite against a common threat. What actually happened was a little different from that: dedicated individuals, each with a particular style and strength, have stepped forward and hung tough.

11

THE EYE OF THE NEEDLE

All this history and heartache, sweat and substance, eventually had to funnel its way down to a point, and squeeze through the eye of a needle into the opportunity presented in one day, at one meeting, for one hour, in one briefing room at the Pentagon in Washington DC.

The day was June 30, 1994. The meeting's purpose: to convince the Deputy Secretaries of the Army and Air Force that they should pay to control pollution at (if not clean up) the Massachusetts Military Reservation.

Bourne Selectman Haydon Coggeshall, elected to serve in town hall after working for IBM for 25 years, was the only person not on a military payroll who attended the meeting. Coggeshall sat in as the representative both of his town, and the public beyond the borders of his town. He lent credibility, and he was someone the military knew was no loose cannon; his approach, as co-chairman of the Senior Management Board, had been dispassionate, deliberate, and cooperative. Joel Feigenbaum could rail that Coggeshall at times "makes a mockery of public participation" in the way he conducted meetings, but Haydon took all that with a large grain of salt. What mattered was that a comprehensive proposal was on the Pentagon's table, and the moment was at hand.

"Believe me," he smiles, "for a small-town kid from Bourne, it was quite a show."

156

Two weeks earlier, Coggeshall had flown to Andrews Air Force Base for a dry run. People who had been through it all before listened to a mock presentation, and urged what Haydon refers to as "showbiz changes: make the slides easier to read. Don't ever say, 'This will shorten completion time for the project,' say how it will be shortened. Don't ever say, 'This will save dollars,' say how many dollars will be saved. Make sure the last slide in the presentation is of such a quality that if it stands alone, there will be no questions." Risk assessments, alternative treatment strategies, legal considerations, all had to be considered.

On the morning of June 29, the Massachusetts contingent flew into Washington. The state chain of command, running from Ernie Keating to Adjutant General Vezina, was present. The federal chain of command, running from Dan Santos through Gary Hinkle to Dave Van Gasbeck (new head of the IRP program nationwide) was present. What was absent was the document itself, the Plume Response Plan that so many people had worked on so hard for many weeks. Consultants from Texas, hired by the military, had run into problems making the necessary last-minute changes. A courier boarded a commercial flight for Washington with instructions to hand-carry the carton of documents; no checked baggage, or no flight. He made it to Washington, and rented a car which promptly broke down. He reached the Air Force base, and got lost trying to find the IRP office. The documents finally arrived at 1:45 pm for a 3:30 briefing at the Pentagon.

The Pentagon is a long way from Cape Cod. It is an intimidating complex, the five-pointed star, five levels with five rings on each level, the halls and walls covered with original artwork, 30,000 people working in office after office. The business of this particular group on this particular day was conducted in one of untold many briefings rooms.

"About 30 other people" were there, Coggeshall remembers, "half with eagles on their collars, half civilians." Once again, more than one chain of command was present; the Army and the Air Force each had links which led to the level of deputy secretary.

"I had an expectation," remembers Dan Santos, "that this was a formality, that all the legwork was done, the skids greased, whatever cliche you want to use. I figured it would be an hour, some obligatory remarks, and then they'd pass approval.

"It didn't happen that way." "The presentation was a battleground," says Haydon.

157

"Figuratively, it was a blood fest. They really attacked; mostly the Army people."

"Everyone on the Air Force side had been briefed, right up the chain of command," says Santos. "But the Army had broken down at my level—the project management group."

Dave Van Gasbeck, newly appointed to be in charge of the IRP program nationwide, was making the presentation. "Van Gasbeck did the battling," says Haydon, "and believe me he fought. They came after him on legal issues: 'Is this in compliance with CERCLA? Will EPA approve it? Prove that—how do we know? Has there been peer review? What are the alternatives?'"

Santos remembers the higher-ups on the Army side saying that they needed to step back, and to take a good close look at this, "and I'm ready to burst out, 'What the —— have you been doing for two months?' I'll tell you, the Army never agreed with this whole process. I think this was their way of sticking it to us."

"It was almost like they didn't realize what was going on," says Coggeshall. The size of the plumes, particularly the landfill plume, "blew their minds. They were realizing that this will be the biggest cleanup they ever got involved in."

Coggeshall remembers having three questions he wanted to stick with, and make sure got on the table: Do you buy in? Will you pay for it? Will you do it in the time frame? By the end of the hour, he had the impression that there would be money to pay for design of a treatment system—maybe. But more peer review would be necessary to make sure that the plan would work. In short, he didn't have an answer to his questions.

"Van Gasbeck was furious," Coggeshall recalls. "He'd been attacked."

As the meeting broke up, the Massachusetts contingent was discouraged. "I was quite down at that point," says Coggeshall. He spoke with Congressman Studds, but didn't really know what to say. The scope of the problem was much clearer to these people, that was for sure. But was there a commitment? No way.

Meanwhile, fast footwork had replaced shuffling in the hallways. The Army's mid-level brass was getting buttonholed, and the message was clear: You guys have been involved in this process. Your people might not have bothered to tell you, but they've signed off on the plan. The gist was basically, "Hey, let me tell you a few things you should know." And because some of this talk was coming from Dave Van Gasbeck, who had put in years of work in the Pentagon, there was some added credibility to the informal communication.

In football parlance, there had been a fumble near the goal line. If this had been fourth down, the project might still be slogging through review and red tape. But Congressman Studds' office had set up one more play. Early the following morning, the key players moved up one more level, to a pre-arranged meeting with a woman named Sherri Goodman. Goodman's formal title is Deputy Undersecretary of Defense for Environmental Security. As such, she is responsible for any and all environmental cleanup done with Pentagon money; in essence, her office controls the budgets for this work, which are distributed to the Army and Air Force.

Once again, Coggeshall was at the meeting, which this time was much smaller. "She asked some perceptive, pointed questions," he remembers, "mostly about risk. She wanted information broken down by plume, and she wanted to know what happens if you let them go." Coggeshall wasn't surprised to see the Air Force weigh in with full support, but he was amazed to see a "total change" from the Army side. "I was shocked. They were totally supportive." Informally, the message had gotten through.

"I asked my three questions," Haydon continues. "And she asked me, very politely, to leave the room. I said all right. About 10 minutes later they called me back, and she said, 'The answers to those three questions are yes, yes, and yes. There is a compelling need, so we buy in. Will we fund it? Yes. And the time frame?' At that point she hesitated. . . but a colonel on her staff stepped in and said yes to that too."

After the frustration of the previous afternoon, it was almost too easy, too good. But it was for real. As the meeting broke up, Goodman stopped Coggeshall, "and we chatted a bit. She said, 'Do you know my parents live in Orleans?' . . . Meanwhile, the Army guy is telling me that we did a fine job, the check's in the mail." On the Air Force side, Haydon adds, people were saying that the process used to involve the public in this decision "should act as a model for other situations nationwide."

It was a remarkable coup, a multi-million-dollar score. At every level, people fell into line. Without unanimous support, from the state military hierarchy all the way to the region's Congressman getting the crucial Pentagon player involved, the proposal would never have cleared the bureaucratic hurdles.

"It sounds ridiculous, given how long it has taken," says Steve Schwadron, chief of staff for Congressman Studds. "But this is farther, faster than anyone anywhere else in the country has gotten."

The key to it all was the strength of the process which led to the plan's creation. Without public involvement, without years of knocking on doors and sitting around tables, this one project at the edge of the continent would never have survived the Pentagon pressure, where cleanup money is tight and environmental problems monumental. It took years, but a foundation had been built strong enough to withstand a real battering.

If there is any doubt about the necessity and authority of community support, consider the following anecdote: back in 1993, a year earlier, Dan Santos and his boss at the time, Ron Watson, approached a very similar cast of Pentagon characters, in a similar briefing, with the idea that the plumes seeping out of the Massachusetts Military Reservation should be contained as quickly as possible. The idea was fundamentally the same, but there was no political buttress for it, no groundwork laid. The result of that meeting? "They shot us down," as Dan Santos puts it.

From a public policy point of view, there is something deeply disquieting about this closed-door, back channel way of determining who gets the public's money. Congress is supposed to decide such things; nothing in the handbook about democracy explains that the case gets pleaded in a Pentagon briefing room, that the judge and jury are mid-level bureaucrats rather than elected peers.

But this is the truth of it. Congress will pass a budget which devotes nearly $2 billion for military cleanup next year. That pie could get cut into a thousand pieces, easily. Who gets a sliver, who gets a slice, who gets nothing at all—these are the decisions that matter, site by site.

And so anywhere in the country where a military base needs to be "remediated," sooner or later the complicated scenario of that place will have to be distilled into a one-hour presentation, delivered far from home. It will have to survive a severe, anonymous test, run a gauntlet no Founding Father ever imagined. It will have to punch a hole through a huge brown paper bag which is the federal bureaucracy.

There are reasons why Cape Cod made it this time, why this group is now looking at designs and timetables rather than yet more ad hoc committees and CERCLA uncertainty.

These are the lessons of activism.

12

LESSONS LEARNED, LESSONS APPLIED

The Massachusetts Military Reservation is one of hundreds of US bases around the country (and the world) with major environmental problems. So in many ways, the people who live around this installation are farther down a road that many others will have to travel in the decades ahead. Not everything done here can be transplanted with success, but much can. And if their advice can create shortcuts, and speed this tortuously slow process, then so much the better.

For Joel Feigenbaum, the crucial first step is getting your hands on information. "Read the Remedial Investigation Reports," he urges. Every base in the country should have some form of environmental reporting on file, because Congress mandated that this basic information be gathered.

If base personnel are reluctant to release this information, "get access through the Freedom of Information Act," he recommends. This federal law often is invoked by journalists to force the release of information which has been hidden, which might be embarrassing or even incriminating, but is no true threat to national security. Simply write a letter to the base public relations office (or commander's office if there is no public affairs contact), and explain that this is a "Freedom of Information Act request" for any records or reports pertaining to the base's environmental health. Any citizen must then be provided with the relevant information on the subject in question. This only makes sense; after all, these reports were funded by public tax dollars. Failure to release this information in a timely fashion, or to explain why national security forbids such release, can result in serious penalties.

"Then you have to analyze these things," Feigenbaum continues, and get help if necessary, "because there's a great tendency to minimize."

Once the wheel is rolling, "the biggest lesson is persistence," says Sue Nickerson. "Persistence, and not being easily mollified by bones being thrown out in the process. You need people willing to dig in and go toe to toe with the military. Because there is definitely a wall to get through."

For Stephanie Adams, the wall can be between you and your neighbor as much as between the community and the base. "Don't be afraid to have people calling you names," she urges. "Stick with your beliefs."

Susan Walker agrees that "persistence pays off. . . (because) if you come in for six months and then you're gone, you're just out of their hair."

To build a structure that supports a longer-term commitment, Walker advises people to "form a group, and make some decisions on how to operate." Come up with a name for the organization. Always have a member at every public meeting. Get as much information as possible, and then "let the political figures know you're concerned, and get the politicians to work for you. That will make the military more respectful of the activists. Be reasonable, but don't be afraid to ask tough questions."

At public meetings, Walker continues, one person can be dismissed, but "three people can make it pretty strong. Organize what to ask ahead of time... Use letters to the editor and letters to politicians.

"And if you're not happy," she concludes, "go over the head of the person you're talking to."

Richard Hugus agrees, though he puts it in starker terms. "The only thing that accomplishes anything is constant pressure," he says. "It's political pressure that matters."

"You need someone like Joel," Stephanie Adams continues. "A person with passion, and expertise. You need at least one person, maybe more, who stays with it. And then, getting the legitimate political process to work in concert is crucial. It's a matter of keeping at the elected officials, finding political and legal avenues."

"Make sure to focus on the goal," urges George Crombie from the Massachusetts Department of Environmental Protection. "Get away from CERCLA. Focus on what you really want to accomplish."

From his desk at the Sandwich Water District, Bob Kreykenbohm adds another perspective. He believes that solid information, as much as solid politics, can move the issue. With that idea in mind, he convinced his own town's taxpayers to spend $300,000 for independent studies to find out what was going on near Snake Pond. That move, he is convinced, gave him credibility and a lever into the military process.

"The key thing is to get some money and prove them wrong," says Kreykenbohm. "Then they'll listen to you."

Falmouth Selectman Virginia Valiela believes that the combination of information and organization is crucial. She also urges the military to pay more than lip service to the unique process which brought people like her to the table. It took years, but once selectmen and activists were included, once meetings were opened up, a momentum developed.

"We are a model, we're a first," says Valiela. "And they say, 'Here's a base that has all these legal problems, but they're not in court. What's the secret?' Well, pay attention! The secret is the technical, community approach."

The great benefit of this tactic is that stereotypes begin to break down—in both directions. The cliches of "the angry citizenry and the faceless military," as Sue Nickerson puts it, dissolve into personalities, and those distinctions can be crucial in terms of understanding whom to approach, who is open to change. "When there are names and faces on both sides, more of a working relationship can be created," she adds.

Different approaches on how to reach that personal level remain. Ernie Keating, for instance, believes it is important for neighbors to approach the military carefully, without a demanding tone, requesting participation:

"I would suggest that people go in, and ask the base official. Say, 'We would like to ask you to be a part of a community advisory panel on environmental issues, and we want to include your base.' It would be hard for the guy to say no. And I think that would start a chain of events."

But even someone like Ron Watson, who ran the Air Force's IRP program nationwide until his recent retirement, who was tough and stubborn regarding some issues for the Cape Cod base, now believes that a hat-in-hand tone is not necessary or appropriate.

"We would often talk about speaking as a teacher, to maintain control," Watson remembers, referring to strategizing prior to open meetings and discussions with community activists. "But it's not that. You need to try to speak as an equal. We have to learn how to work these things out."

Ask Watson what his advice would be to community groups, and he sounds remarkably like the people he resisted for years. "Share information," he urges. "Don't duplicate. Put technical staffs together. Don't reinvent the wheel time after time. And we have to strive to trust each other. That can fix a great many problems.

"Sometimes I wonder," he muses, "if the military isn't getting pushed into community management programs."

Dave Van Gasbeck, who replaced Watson, believes that the military must move in that direction. "This is such an important issue, the partnering, that it will become a measure of merit" in the IRP program, he predicts.

Van Gasbeck believes that cleanup projects around the country will use a structure similar to the one hammered out on Cape Cod. Civic leaders will be asked to join "action teams" which examine specific issues, as well as "management boards" which recommend action. Meetings will be open. When Van Gasbeck refers to this as "a measure of merit," he is saying (in a Washington sort of way) that bases which don't do this kind of groundwork are not going to get the money they need to clean up.

"This is the cutting edge," he concludes. "This is a test of how it will work."

"I'm still not sure there's an appreciation of what this structure can accomplish," says George Crombie, "or an appreciation of the sophistication it takes to keep this structure together." He worries that once a plan is in place, federal officials think that the community involvement side of the work is no longer necessary. Suddenly there is a feeling that "you can drive this project like a spike."

That attitude is a fatal mistake, Crombie continues. "People like Joel (Feigenbaum) and Susan (Nickerson) have fought tenaciously to get to where we are today," he says. "You can't throw these people away, and put them in the back row. You can't do that. They're part of this thing. They're part of the solution. Without them, it's doomed to failure."

Congressional staffperson Mark Forest believes that community groups can't "wait for Washington to get their act together." He urges people not to be docile about accepting bureaucratic definitions of how change should happen.

"Don't let that CERCLA snake dictate this process," he advises. "If the rules are getting in the way, fight like hell to change those rules. Don't feel you have to be stuck with this snake." Multiple problems on one base don't have to be approached piecemeal; they can be grouped together and attacked as one: "We need to have success stories, and we need to build models and policies based on success stories. Maybe our approach can be helpful to others."

As the base's point man in this process for more than four years, Dan Santos has a unique perspective. He has come a long way from 1990, when he "followed orders" and opposed open meetings, when he repeated Ron Watson's position that the landfill plume should be allowed to seep all the way to the sea. As he moves into the private sector, it seems that the process he helped engineer—a trial by fire, some would say—has changed him a great deal:

"My advice to other groups around the country would be: demand involvement up front, in all aspects of the process. That's what's been done here. And it worked. The community has decided how we're going to look at the ponds, and manage these plumes.

"How do you convince people (in the military) of this? Now you have a precedent. You point here and say, 'They did it, and this is the same government. Why can't we participate? Why can't we have open meetings?' There are no good answers why not.

"It really comes down to two things: it's my community, and it's my money. I want a voice."

13

CONCLUSIONS, AND THE FUTURE

For decades, benefit and harm have been created side by side.

Into the next century, prospects for opportunity and disaster move hand in hand.

The Massachusetts Military Reservation is both resource, and albatross.

Environmentally, this base has the amazing capacity to be the worst of what we have on Cape Cod, and (outside the National Seashore) the best. It has created mammoth problems with profound damage, problems which are impossible to solve and very difficult to contain. At the same time, it has the resources to pay back, to restore much of what it has taken away, to step into the vanguard of the movement to protect and defend the natural security of Cape Cod. What has become a symbol of pollution could be a reservoir, a buffer, a guarantee for a better future.

What we choose to do next cannot restore the health of anyone damaged by what has happened at the base over the years. We cannot erase people's fears, or even remove the contamination now in the ground. That will take the passing of a generation.

But we can learn from our mistakes, and this education can go on at many levels.

Technically, there are things to be learned about how to fight pollution; this

166

base could become a giant laboratory, a high-tech research and development center searching for innovative solutions that could be applied elsewhere. Meanwhile, the sad truth is that thousands of acres of the facility have not yet been investigated, and could conceal yet more danger.

Emotionally, psychologically, politically, the lessons have everything to do with openness, participation, and creating a chain of command which is foreign to the traditional military mindset. The military is no democracy, but the military serves a democracy. Any decision with implications beyond internal structure, whether it's about going to war or cleaning up pollution, must be reached by stretching through a democratic process.

Honest thought about the future of the Massachusetts Military Reservation begins by addressing a key question which hovers over all discussion. Even raising the question raises hackles among some military personnel, who worry about their jobs much as any factory worker frets over rumors of a plant closure. Yet the question must be asked:

Should this military base be closed? Indeed, given the end of the Cold War, shrinking defense budgets, and a lengthening list of bases around the country which are being told to shut their doors, the first question is even more basic:

Why hasn't this base been closed already? For starters, military sources say that it is the Coast Guard, more than anything else, which is keeping this base alive. The Coast Guard's function is considered vital, essential, and high-profile. Coast Guard personnel need housing, which the base provides. They need a convenient takeoff and landing area for their aerial sea rescues, which the base provides. They need a center for training, and organizing marine patrols, which the base provides. From a public relations perspective, every time a boater or fisherman is plucked out of the roiling ocean by a Coast Guard rescue team, there is one more front-page argument in favor of keeping the base open.

The second major justification which weighs heavily in military thinking is PAVE PAWS, the Air Force's radar facility. Controversy continues to swirl about how these microwave radiation beams might affect the health of people nearby, yet the Air Force maintains that the installation is a crucial piece of our national defense. Given that the primary mission of PAVE PAWS is to detect submarine-launched nuclear missiles, and given that the defunct Soviet Union is the only hostile power with that capability, the importance of PAVE PAWS seems diminished. The time will likely come when it goes the way of the Texas Towers, or the BOMARC missile, and becomes obsolete. But that time, says the Air Force, is not now.

To a lesser degree, the landing strips themselves create value. They are a resource for everything from jet fighter training to a spot for the space shuttle to make an emergency landing. Given the reality of diminished open space, and complaints about noise, they would be virtually impossible to replace; these F-15s have the Atlantic Ocean's air space to fool around in, a vast expanse with no community to impact—save the seagulls.

Yet take all this together, add the Army National Guard's "weekend warrior" training, and still the justification feels thin for holding 22,000 acres of Cape Cod in military hands— one-tenth of one of the most beautiful and popular peninsulas in the country. So it is not altogether surprising to learn that there is one more reason why this base has not shown up on any of the closure lists yet, a reason that is deeply ironic yet makes sense when seen through federal eyes.

"When bases were chosen for closing," begins Ron Watson, former head of the Air Guard's IRP program, "the amount of contamination was part of the rating process."

Wouldn't that move Otis up on the list, because so much pollution has been found there?

Just the opposite, says Watson: "Contamination KEPT you as a military base."

The reason? "We needed to return land that could be redeveloped rapidly," Watson explains. "And if the land was contaminated, you couldn't do that. So it was a very important thing. . . If you pull the military out, and can't return the land for other uses, it's really a double whammy for the community."

So economics argues in favor of keeping polluted bases open, because legally a Superfund site like the Massachusetts Military Reservation cannot simply be converted to other uses; it has to be cleaned up first. In effect, decades worth of spills and dumping now help secure the military's position at the base.

The ironies only get deeper. Dave Van Gasbeck, who succeeded Watson, worked directly on base closure issues in the Pentagon before he moved to the IRP program. He confirms much of Watson's analysis, adding, "If you can clean up quickly, it (the facility) could transition to other viable uses more quickly. But a 20 or 30-year cleanup is a different problem."

Once again, it seems to be the fate of Cape Cod's base to find itself at the cutting edge of change in the military. This time, says Van Gasbeck, the "different problem" created here has forced a re-evaluation of how base closures in general should be handled:

"I think where we are now," he says, referring to Pentagon thinking, "is that you can transition permanently once a site is remediated, or once treatment is in place."

If that indeed becomes policy, then the fate of the Massachusetts reservation will once again be on the table. Regardless, Van Gasbeck stresses a key point:

"We have to clean up, whether it is open or closed. We would still have that obligation."

The state military leadership clearly is interested in maintaining, and even expanding its operations while the cleanup proceeds. "From a selfish point of view, we're concerned about our survival," says Adjutant General Raymond Vezina. "Part of our survival is to be active in the community, and we're not going to give that up to anybody. . . Joel (Feigenbaum) won't be happy until we're out of there lock, stock, and barrel. But I don't see that happening."

"Modernization" plans proposed for the base include improving Coast Guard operations, building a new "Infantry Squad Battle Course," and creating a facility to teach soldiers how to fight the likes of drug dealers and "urban guerrillas" in a makeshift "city environment" complete with things like a "storm drain simulator" and 17 buildings, "some constructed to simulate a rubbilized effect."

If all this sounds like a bit of a stretch, it may be because the domestic military is groping for new mandates, searching for new definitions. "There's going to be a military for as long as we're around," muses Ron Watson. "But what the new mission is, I have a hard time understanding now that the Cold War is over. I mean, I was in the Defense Department for 30 years. . . but given present realities, I believe we should not be looking for the military to be there (on Cape Cod) long term. In my opinion, the military in the latter part of this century is not a permanent facility."

"To me, a reduction in military activity out there would be important to this community," says Susan Nickerson from the Association for the Preservation of Cape Cod. "To dedicate a portion of the base as a conservation reserve makes a lot of sense. For water resources, for habitat protection, it's an opportunity to create a wildlife refuge. . . Whether the whole base should be closed is another question. But I think a portion of the base should be set aside for preservation, and water protection."

The northern 15,000 or so acres of the base is its frontier, its wild open space. The runways, housing, and industrial activity all are clumped to the south—as is the pollution identified to date. But the Impact Area is in the north, and that complicates the issue.

"That area is a complete blank as far as environmental knowledge goes," says Richard Hugus. "It's critical now. We're looking for clean water sources to replace what's been polluted. And the base insists on not only using this (impact) area, but increasing its use. . . They don't want to lose that Impact Area. If they do, they can't have a 'magnet base' for New England, which is the plan." For Hugus, the Impact Area has become the key: stop weapons firing there. Investigate to see if secret dumping or other military activity has contaminated the groundwater. If it hasn't, use this northern area for well sites, to return clean water to the surrounding towns. And then shut down the base, and convert it to civilian uses.

A measure of how far the debate has moved in recent years is found in General Vezina's comments: "I'm very receptive to doing additional well testing," he says, "with the goal of coming up with additional well sites." But that doesn't mean artillery needs to be shut down, in his opinion. Vezina sees potential in "the northern portion of the post. . . that's not close to the Impact Area."

"It would take an enormous amount of resources just to make that place safe to walk around in," says Dan Santos. He suspects that future well sites exist on the base, and to develop them would be one way to pay back for decades of unintentional damage. But he believes commercial or residential development of the huge woodland would be a profound mistake.

"The base should be open space," says Santos. "To develop it would be the worst thing you could do environmentally for the region."

The frustration about the plan now in place to deal with the plumes is that it is not the BEST thing that could be done environmentally for the region. To be sure, there is fundamental justice to it—the military should clean up what it polluted. But in truth the technical expertise does not exist to erase these gigantic underground smudges. And leaving it at containment, for $250 million, with wells and pumps and pipes and filters necessary into the next century, is a profoundly unsatisfying result.

In the ideal world, a quarter of a billion dollars could buy an awful lot of environmental benefit: more open space, a string of sewage treatment facilities, new wells, you name it. Instead, when all this is in place we will have pushed back a serious threat, but not addressed the future.

It has been said before, but it bears repeating. More than anything, the situation at this base proves a deceptively simple maxim: if you know what you're doing is causing harm, and don't have a clue how to clean it up, then stop doing it. And before anyone gets self-righteous in judging the deeds of the past, it would be worthwhile to consider all the things being done today, in the name of security or jobs or progress, which we are leaving to another generation to worry about and pay for. From nuclear waste to plastic garbage, from ocean dumping to orbiting outer space debris, the list is long—and we no longer have the excuse of ignorance.

Throughout its history, the Massachusetts Military Reservation has served a variety of military purposes. It also has served as a metaphor, a symbol of the national situation. There has been nothing planned about this; it just kind of happened that way, decade by decade.

The base could continue to play this role into the next century. To do so, it now seems clear that we would have to rethink our relationship to this pollution which has been dumped in our laps. We would have to pull opportunity out of disaster, a new rabbit from an old hat. Open space and uncontaminated groundwater are two resources the military base could offer. A third resource, strange as it sounds, could be the polluted sites themselves.

Where better to study how contamination moves underground? Where better to experiment with new ways of treating pollution? Where better to bring industry interested in profit, and science interested in innovation, together to work on problem solving? Where better to generate jobs that are environmentally friendly, to replace jobs that were not?

The military base has the space to create a research and development facility and still leave 15,000 acres open. It has proximity to world-class scientists and academics in Boston and Woods Hole, with an airport to boot. And, of course, it has the raw material to work on, the most common and widespread types of environmental pollution, from sewage to petroleum to solvents.

Call it the campus of Hazardous Waste University; call it the corporate headquarters of Hazardous Waste, Inc. Either way, don't call it a pipe dream; in early 1994 the district's Congressman, Gerry Studds, was able to win a federal commitment of $1 million to begin design on a facility which could house and support research and development on the base.

"The site plays into a larger vision," says Mark Forest, Studds' spokesman. "We should use these sites as laboratories, no question."

In terms of the larger vision, the attempt to steer this military base toward invention and innovation links national security and natural security in a way that makes a lot of sense. If there is a threat to the "American way of life," as people have described the culture we fight to protect, it is no longer military in nature. It is economic. Environmental technology is a crucial growth field with potential customers on every continent. Ask people in the know, and they will say that already the United States is lagging behind Germany and Japan in developing that technology. For the federal government to help private enterprise push forward, using places like the Massachusetts Military Reservation as a new kind of "base," would be a fitting and wise way to champion a redefined national defense.

But in the meantime (and that might be a long time), the military's responsibility for this Superfund site also needs to be redefined. Yes, the plumes must be contained, as quickly and effectively as possible. Yes, investigations must continue to make sure more of the past's dangerous toxics aren't seeping through the ground. Yes, care must be used to make sure today's activities don't leave behind new plumes, new legacies.

And yes, the public should be involved in every decision that has to do with any of these issues.

The struggle to open up this military base, and keep it open, is in some ways as important as the cleanup work itself. As rancorous and rocky as the road has been, the Cape Cod community deserves a promise that neither state nor federal officials responsible for this base will revert to the traditional, secretive ways of doing military business.

A structure exists to deliver on that promise, a management board, including selectmen from the four surrounding towns, "teams" of neighbors and technicians seated at the same table and thinking about specific problems like groundwater supplies, or innovative technologies. All this may feel like a mechanical, clunky substitute for fluid, spontaneous communication, but it is a framework that both frames, and works. As much cannot be said of most management/think tank/public policy strategies.

Already, there are signs of a retreat from this commitment. Some had hoped that there would be public discussion before a new head of the local IRP office (Dan Santos' replacement) was chosen. There was no such discussion. The decision was made quickly, behind closed doors. The choice, Mike Minior, was an "insider," well versed in the IRP program and the Pentagon mentality, long on engineering experience but short on community relations in general, or in this Upper Cape community in particular.

At the first meeting of the Senior Management Board after the new appointment, George Crombie watched as many of the old tensions began to resurface, as distrust and friction reared up again. "I sat there, and I almost cried," he says.

Jim Begley, who has worked on cleanup issues at the base since 1986 for the state Department of Environmental Protection, feels that "the basic level of trust we can achieve has a ceiling. It doesn't take much to knock that ceiling right down again, but it takes a lot longer to build it up. . . I don't know if it's the so-called 'military mentality,' but these guys have been in control of other projects, and they weren't told by so-called 'outside groups' what to do, and there may be some resentment about the process."

Minior claims these fears are unfounded. "In my experience, working everywhere from Alaska to Puerto Rico, I've never seen the level of community involvement that exists at Otis. I find it refreshing and welcome."

And he pledges that the Cape experience will be a model: "I agree 100 percent with what my predecessor [Santos] has started. Nationally, this is something we want to establish."

Time will tell. None of this means that Minior was a bad choice, or that he won't do a fine job in the months ahead. But it does mean that a lesson may not have been learned. It is a danger signal that "they want to rein this process back in," to use Dan Santos' words.

Years of pushing and prodding have changed the way some decisions are reached on this military base. It feels like an elastic has been stretched, a circle widened.

But it also feels like that rubber band wants to resume its former shape. To revert now, to shrink back, would be an ugly mistake. It would jeopardize much goodwill built slowly, meeting by meeting, for more than 10 years. It would also jeopardize the cleanup itself, which needs public support and the credibility of outside involvement. It would destroy the great benefit of role model, which this base represents for others around the country. And morally, it would be wrong.

There is a constant temptation at work within this military reservation, a desire to seize up, to harden into a certain form and approach. That's understandable; after all, for generations military training has emphasized structure. The urge to clamp down is so strong it is almost palpable, like an insistent voice in the ear, saying:

Take control. Always announce, never ask. Close the gates. Surrender as little information (to "the enemy") as possible. It's "our" base. These are "our" decisions. "They" should never make demands of "us;" "they" should always trust, respect, and defer.

This attitude did not create the environmental catastrophe we now face; all of us can lay some claim to that. But this attitude did help conceal it. This attitude retarded efforts to clean it up. And this attitude will do nothing to stop the damage now.

Indeed, if this attitude had won out over the past five years, it is safe to say that there would be no approved cleanup plan, no $250 million commitment from the Department of Defense. The local lesson for the military bureaucracy is undeniable: Open up. Loosen up.

The national lesson is just as apparent: the federal bureaucracy has to slim down, and clamp down. The so-called CERCLA process is making millions for contractors, without making much of a dent in the ground. The entire Superfund concept is in jeopardy because the process needs something as dramatic as an aroused citizenry approaching open rebellion to rouse itself to action. Managers of environmental budgets better start looking for results rather than studies, for earth moving rather than paper shuffling, for more chuck for the public buck—or start looking for other work.

During wartime, the military has always prided itself on doing the impossible. Build a city of 50,000 in four months. Invade Normandy. Build an atomic bomb. The word "No" was not part of an acceptable answer. That same attitude should be applied to the national challenge we now face. We need to find ways to clean up our military bases, and the word "No" should not be in the vocabulary of strategy. It may sound strange, but in some respects we have been very lucky here on Cape Cod. We have massive problems, but we don't have the high-level radioactive waste disposal site which was once proposed. We never had an accident (that we know about) with the nuclear bombs at the tips of BOMARC missiles in our back yards. Military activities have harmed the environment and may well have harmed the public health, but in comparison to the worst of the radioactive sites in this country we are in better shape. We can still consider solutions, entertain alternatives, and live on this beautiful peninsula.

In part, we can credit our good fortune to those people who, more than 30 years ago, refused to accept the federal government's notion that a "nuclear park" was a great plus for Cape Cod. They fought that idea tooth and nail, and

174

they are not much different from the activists who challenge the military today, who continue to stretch the elastic and demand more of most everything: more money, more care, more information, more involvement, more results.

There is a strong temptation to second-guess almost everything about this situation, and everyone involved in it. We can castigate a previous generation for what they did and didn't do. We can question motives today. Indeed, virtually every single person interviewed, regardless of position, inside and outside the base, at some point darkly ascribed a "hidden agenda" to someone else: power, control, patronage, profit, anti-military bias, psychological foibles, you name it.

This is not to say that such issues don't exist; as the old saying goes, even paranoids have enemies. But to focus on and fret about real and perceived conspiracies is to take the eye off the prize:

Everyone deserves to live free of fear, free of threat, free of danger. That holds true whether the hostile power is overseas—or underground. From World Wars to Cold War, the Massachusetts Military Reservation has played its part as the battlefields moved, and the terms of victory shifted. Americans are not used to fighting on their own turf, but we have a battle on our hands now which should make us forget our differences, rip up the red tape, and confront this invisible, insidious enemy within. Cleaning up our military bases should be a top national priority. The experience at Cape Cod's base is an early skirmish, tactically full of important lessons, in a fight which will soon be taken up throughout the country.

ABOUT THE AUTHOR

Seth Rolbein has written about Cape Cod for nearly 20 years, first as a reporter for *The Register* newspaper, later as editor of the *Cape Cod Business Journal* and as a contributor to *Boston Magazine, Yankee Magazine, The Boston Herald Sunday Magazine,* and other publications.

Two of his books have been published by St. Martin's Press. "Sting of the Bee," a novel, was set in Jamaica. "Nobel Costa Rica," non-fiction, explored the history, culture, and politics of that Central American nation.

His journalistic work also includes documentaries produced for WGBH-TV, public television in Boston. The subjects have ranged widely; an exploration of Vietnam, a year in the life of Provincetown, an investigation of radioactive waste dumping at sea. His most recent documentary, "Out of Sight, Out of Mind," won an Emmy from the National Academy of Television Arts and Sciences as the best public affairs program aired in New England in 1993.

Presently, Mr. Rolbein lives in Truro. On clear days, looking across Cape Cod Bay, he can just make out the ridge of land which is the shoulder of Cape Cod, where the Massachusetts Military Reservation is located.